The Three Sorrowful Tales of Erin

OTHER HEROIC RETELLINGS FROM
HISTORY AND LEGEND
=====

HEROES OF GREECE AND TROY
Roger Lancelyn Green

MYTHS OF THE NORSEMEN
Roger Lancelyn Green

GRETTIR THE STRONG
Allen French

XENOPHON'S ADVENTURE
Geoffrey Household

BEOWULF
Rosemary Sutcliff

THE HOUND OF ULSTER
Rosemary Sutcliff

THE KNIGHTS OF THE GOLDEN TABLE
E. M. Almedingen

CAESAR'S GALLIC WAR
Olivia Coolidge

THE BURNING OF NJAL
Henry Treece

THE TREASURE OF SIEGFRIED
E. M. Almedingen

SONS OF THE VOLSUNGS
Dorothy Hosford

The Three Sorrowful Tales of Erin

F. M. PILKINGTON

Francis Meredith

with drawings by
VICTOR AMBRUS

NEW YORK
HENRY Z. WALCK, INCORPORATED
1966

To
BEATRICE M. BLACKWOOD
with love and deep gratitude.
Magnis munera parva libens

64/106

Contents

Author's Note, 7

Contents (*continued*)

AUTHOR'S NOTE

These three legends belong to a group of Irish sagas known as "the Three Sorrows of Story-telling" (or "the Three Sorrowful Tales of Erin"), and are part of the mythological cycle.

Deirdre is perhaps the best known of the three—her story is also known in Scotland, and survived down to the twentieth century in Scottish oral tradition.

The whole cycle is very ancient, and probably dates from the ninth century in writing; but it is important to remember that the oral tradition must go much further back—possibly to about the third century, when it was kept alive by bards and Druids.

The poems are of the Edda variety; that is, they deal with situations and emotions, and consist mainly of speeches. They belong to the Heroic Age of verse.

The poem used to describe Deirdre's house in Alba does not belong to the legend, but the description was so apt that I took the liberty to borrow some of the verses from "the King and the Hermit", an early Irish monastic lyric, dating from the ninth century, and to be found in the Oxford Book of Early Irish Lyrics, 1962. Thanks are due to the Clarendon Press, Oxford, for permission to reproduce it.

The Knights of the Red Branch came from the great race of Ir, or Iranians, and belonged chiefly to the northern provinces of Ireland, having their home at Emania, the then capital of Ulster, which endured for 600 years. The race were perhaps better known as the Clan Rury (Clanna Rudhraighe), so named after Rudhraighe, a great monarch of Ireland who lived some three hundred years before Christ.

An "eric" was a fine paid for murder either to the relatives or friends of the dead; but it was sometimes the penalty for other crimes.

"Geasa" were injunctions, or solemn vows, taken either voluntarily by those who wished to do so, or imposed by others with a person's consent. It was also possible to put someone under "geasa" to perform or grant a reasonable request; and that person might not refuse to accept the "geasa" without loss of honour.

F. M. Pilkington
Brookleaze, Nettlebridge, Bath
5 March, 1965

THE FATE OF THE
CHILDREN OF TUIREANN

1. How the Fomorians came into Erin

VERY FAR back in the world's history, the green isle of Erin was ruled over by the people known as Tuatha De Danann, and it is known that they were well skilled in all magical arts, and there were many famous men of that race whose names are remembered to this day, and among them Nuada of the Silver Hand.

Now Nuada was king of Erin; and at this time the men of Erin were much harried and oppressed by the Fomorians, sea-robbers from Lochlann in the far north—and they were forced to pay tribute to the Fomorians, and this tribute was taken by tax on querns, and on all kneading-troughs, and baking-flags; and no man dared refuse to pay his share lest he had the nose cut off from his face; and the tribute was paid once a year on the Hill of Usna where the king had his dwelling.

One day it came about that a great gathering of nobles and people was held by Nuada of the Silver Hand on the Hill of Usna, for it was near to the day when the tribute must be paid.

And the people had not long been assembled when they saw a fine company of warriors all riding on white horses coming towards them, and at the fore front rode a young hero who held himself straight and stately, and whose face shone with a light as glorious as a rising sun; and this youth was Lugh the Long-Handed, and he led the Fairy Host from Tir Tairrngire, the Land of Promise, which was ruled over by Mannanan Mac Lir, the sea-god; and with him were his foster-brothers, the sons of Mannanan.

Splendidly indeed was Lugh arrayed—he wore Mannanan's coat of mail, shining brightly as silver, which no weapon could pierce; on his breast was Mannanan's breast-plate, and his helmet was made of red-gold, ornamented in front with glittering jewels. Mannanan's sword, the Answerer, hung at his left side, and so terrible was this weapon that no one wounded by it ever recovered, and those who saw it flashing before them in combat were stricken by a deadly weakness. He rode on Mannanan's mare, Enbarr of the Flaming Mane, whose white coat was dazzling to behold; no one who sat upon her back had ever been killed, for she moved as swiftly as the clear, cold green wind of spring —and could travel as easily by sea as on land.

So this goodly company came quickly to the place were the king of Erin sat, surrounded by the Tuatha De Danann, and greetings were spoken and friendly words passed from one to another.

In no long time then, another company was seen approaching in the distance; but when they drew nearer, there was small likeness to the first—for these were grim and surly warriors, of a wild and fierce appearance. And they were of the number of nine nines, and were the tax-gatherers of the Fomorians come to demand the yearly tribute from the men of Erin.

Now when they had reached the place where Nuada the king sat, he rose, and all the people assembled with him did likewise, for there was a great dread among all the Tuatha De Danann of these Fomorians—and none dare even to break a stick, or hunt a deer without their consent.

Then Lugh the Long-Handed spoke to the king, and he said, "Why do you stand up for this hateful-seeming company when ye did not rise for us?"

And Nuada answered, "We dare not do otherwise—for let you know that if so much as an infant remained seated before them, they would take it as a reason to deal death among us."

When Lugh heard these words he was silent for a while, and then he said, "By Mannanan's sword, I feel a great longing to slay these people." Then again, after musing for a little time further, he said, "I have a great desire to destroy them."

"Evil indeed is the thought, and worse would be the deed," exclaimed the king, "for the Fomorians would gather together a mighty host to send against us, and we should perish utterly."

But Lugh was provoked beyond all reason by this speech, and he cried angrily, "Long have ye been oppressed in this manner, but I will surely put an end to it without further delay."

So saying, he sprang among the Fomorians, and so fearful and sudden was his onslaught that he dealt red slaughter among them, slaying all save nine, who had run to Nuada for protection.

Then Lugh put up his sword in the scabbard, and he said to the nine Fomorians, "Gladly would I slay you also, robbers and murderers, but it is my wish that you return quickly to your king and tell him your story—and spread the tale among other strangers that they may leave us of the Tuatha De Danann in peace lest they meet the same ending."

Now the king of the Fomorians was Balor of the Mighty Blows; and he was also known as Balor of the Evil Eye, for he had one eye which could strike a man dead, or turn him to stone, and so Balor kept that eye covered except when he wished to use it against his enemies.

And when the nine men came to him, and told him their story from beginning to end, Balor asked if any among them could tell him the name of the strange noble-seeming youth who had slain their companions, and they answered, "No."

Then Kethlenda, wife to Balor, spoke, and she said, "I know well the name of this youth—for he must be the Ildana, or man of many skills, Lugh the Long-Handed, son of our daughter Ethlenn. And in long past days it was foretold that when he should appear in Erin our hold over the Tuatha De Danann should be ended."

When Balor heard these words, he rose up, and called a great council of all the nobles and chief men of the Fomorians; and among these were the twelve sons of Balor, and his queen, Kethlenda of the Crooked Teeth; Ebb and Sencab sons of Neid; Tinna the Mighty of Triscadal; Satal of the Large Heels; Luath the Story-teller; Loskenn of the Bare Knees, Lobas the druid, and many more, with nine prophetic poets and philosophers. And to this assembly the nine tax-collectors told their tale—and it was heard with surprise and anger—and after the matter had been debated for a time, Bres, one of the sons of Balor rose, and said, "O my father, and ye nobles and chieftains—give me leave to go to Erin with seven great impenetrable battalions of Fomorians; and I will do battle with the Ildana Lugh, and I promise to bring you his head as a gift."

And although Lobas the druid reminded Bres and the company of the ancient prophecy, and warned them not to be too hasty in their decisions, the chiefs of the Fomorians gave an eager assent to the proposal—and so the matter was settled.

Then great preparations were begun; ships were made ready, and abundant store of food and drink put in them, and many weapons and war stores—and their seams were covered with pitch, and they were made sweet within by frankincense. And messengers were sent over the whole of Lochlann to summon the battalions of warriors together. And when they came to the place where the ships were anchored, they eagerly arrayed themselves in their clothes of combat and valour, and took up their arms, and went up into the ships.

And before they went aboard, Balor of the Mighty Blows spoke to them, and he said, "Give fierce battle to this Ildana Lugh and take his head from his shoulders. And when his hosts are slain, take strong ropes, and put them round the island of Erin which brings us little gain and much trouble, and fasten it strongly to the sterns of your ships. And when you have sailed home with it, put it on the north side of Lochlann, for there none of the Tuatha De Danann will find it."

After that, the hosts set sail, having hoisted their sails of scarlet, and blue, and green. And they threw off their moorings, and went out of the harbour on a strong wind which took them into the arms of the great sea—and so they set their course for Erin.

2. Kian and the Children of Tuireann

THUS, WHEN many days had passed, and the ships had sailed bravely through the restless turmoil of the seas, the shores of Erin came into sight—and Bres ordered a course to be set for the harbour of Eas Dara, which is known today as Ballysodare. And as soon as they had set foot on land the seven battalions went speedily westwards through the province of Connacht, and laid it waste, burning and despoiling all in their path.

Now the king of Connacht at that time was Bove Derg, the son of Dagda; and when the news was brought to him that the sea-robbers had landed an army at Eas Dara, and were spreading destruction and death throughout his lands, he bethought him of Lugh the Long-Handed, for these two were knit close in bonds of friendship.

In this hour Lugh was at Tara of the Kings— and when Bove Derg's messenger gave him the evil tidings, he took his mare Enbarr and set forth very early, at the hour when the point of night meets the day, and did not stay his going until he came to the house of Bove Derg, and gave him gentle greeting.

B

Then said Lugh to the king, "Let you give me one battalion well armed, and with these to help me I will offer battle to the enemy."

But the king answered, "I cannot give you any help, O Lugh, for it is not my wish to avenge a deed which is not done against myself—but if it is in your mind to offer combat to these warriors, I need not fear the outcome."

When Lugh heard these words he was filled with anger, and without speaking further he mounted his horse and rode away to the west; and he had not gone far before he saw three warriors riding to meet him, and they were all three armed, and attired in their war clothing. And when he drew nearer he saw that it was his father, Kian son of Canta, and his father's brothers Cu and Kethen. So they met, and greeted each other. Goodly was the sight of these four tall, handsome chieftains; and strong was the likeness between Lugh and his father, for they both had flashing dark eyes, black as bog-water, and shining, fair-seeming faces, and the colour in their lips and cheeks was brilliant as a holly berry. Over their battle clothing they wore long cloaks of deep, clear green, and golden brooches shaped like wheels to fasten them.

Then Kethen spoke, and he said to Lugh, "What has brought you here so early, and why do you ride in haste?"

And Lugh answered, "Cause enough there is for me to go forward without delay; for the Fomorians have sent an army into Erin, and they have laid waste the lands of Bove Derg, son of Dagda. Well is it that we are met, for it is my wish to offer combat to these robbers, and what aid will you give me in the matter?"

Then each of the three said that he would go into battle with Lugh, and moreover, they would bring with them such help as they could gather. But Lugh answered that first he desired them to separate, and to go to the several places in Erin where the Fairy Host might be found, and summon them quickly.

And now we will leave Lugh the Long-Handed, and follow after his father Kian, who had turned his face to the north, and was riding swiftly to the plain of Moy Murthemna. He had not travelled long over the plain when he saw three warriors, clad in war clothing and carrying their weapons of combat riding towards him, and they were strangers in those parts.

Now these three chieftains were of the race of Tuatha De Danann, and were famous throughout the whole of Erin, and they were the Sons of Tuireann. Their names were Brian, Iuchar, and Iucharba, and these three had a deadly feud with the sons of Canta because of an old quarrel, and it was certain that they could not meet without combat.

When Kian had come a little nearer to them, he recognised them, and he thought to himself, "Now if only my two brothers had been with me we could have had a brave encounter—but seeing that I am only one against three, it is better to avoid a meeting." So he looked around for a hiding place, and seeing a herd of swine at a little distance, he took his golden wand of sorcery and lightly struck himself, so that in an instant he was changed into a pig and ran speedily in among the herd.

Now Brian, the eldest of the Sons of Tuireann, had been watching Kian as he rode towards them, and he said to his brothers, "Do you know what has become of the warrior we saw approaching us, for there is his horse grazing riderless on the plain?"

For Kian in his haste to disappear had forgotten to change his horse into a pig.

Then Iuchar and Iucharba both answered that they did not know where the warrior had gone.

"You are deserving of great blame that you are not more wary while going about the country in time of war," said Brian, "and I will tell you what has happened to that man—he has put a spell on himself and is turned into a pig, and is hidden in that herd yonder. And let you be sure that he is no friend to us."

"Here is ill luck come upon us," they answered, "for the pigs belong to a man of the Tuatha De Danann, and so we may not kill them."

"And even if you could it is not certain that the one we desire to know better might not escape," said Brian, "but I can think of a way to catch him, and if you had given your minds to your learning you could have done that same."

With that, he took a wand of magic virtue from his clothing, and touched each of his brothers in turn—and lo, they were changed into two slender, grey, sharp-nosed hounds; and in that moment they yelped eagerly, and putting their noses to the ground leapt forward with the speed of the black cold north wind, and rushed towards the herd of pigs.

Now when Kian saw them coming, he separated himself from the rest, and ran towards a thicket of birches that grew close at hand; but Brian, who had been on the watch, saw him and ran in front

of Kian, and drove his long, sharp-edged spear through his chest.

Then the pig that was Kian cried out, and said, "This is an ill deed you have done, Brian son of Tuireann, for well you know who I am."

And Brian replied, "You speak as a man and not as a pig, but I do not know who you are."

Then the pig said, "I am Kian, son of Canta, and I am asking you to give me quarter."

At this moment the two hounds ran up, and

Brian quickly changed them into their proper shapes. And when he had told them that it was Kian, son of Canta lying wounded before them, they said, "Willingly will we give you quarter, and sorry we are that this hurt has been done to you without a fair fight."

But Brian, greatly angered by their words, swore that for his part he would show no mercy to Kian, but would not rest until he was slain.

Then Kian spoke, and he said, "If you will not grant me quarter, surely you will let me take my own shape again?"

"That you may do," said Brian, "but do not think to escape us, for we will have your life this day."

So Kian took his own shape, and lay before them, bleeding grievously from the great wound in his chest. And he laughed hoarsely, and said, "Now is it in your minds to slay me, O Children of Tuireann, but I have outwitted you at the last. For had you let me die as a pig you need only have paid eric for a pig—but now you shall pay the full fine for my life—and it will be the greatest ever paid. And the weapons you use against me will tell of the deed to my son, and he will exact eric from you."

"You shall die in this moment," cried Brian furiously, "and we shall not destroy you with the weapons of a warrior, for little have you done to deserve such a death." And with these words he and his brothers threw down their weapons, and snatching up round, cruel-seeming stones of the earth they smote Kian so fiercely that he was slain.

When they saw that he was indeed dead, they dug a hole in the ground to the height of a man, and cast the body into it. But the earth, angered at this evil deed of fratricide, refused to hold the body of Kian, and cast it up again on the surface. Yet a second time they buried him, and again the earth rejected the body. And so it was for six times that the Sons of Tuireann sought to bury Kian, and six times did the earth refuse to receive him. But when they tried for the seventh time, the body rested in its grave.

Then the Children of Tuireann gathered up each one his weapons, and mounted their horses, and set forth once more to follow after Lugh the Long-Handed and take part in the battle. But as they turned away from the grave, they heard a faint sound underfoot, and a hoarse, muffled voice said,

"The blood ye have spilled,
  And the hero ye have killed
Shall follow till your doom be fulfilled."

So they looked at each other in a dreadful silence, and went on their way without further speech.

3. The Defeat
of the Fomorians

NOW WHEN Lugh the Long-Handed had parted
from his father and his uncles, he turned his face
towards the west once more, and rode with the
speed of a flight of wild duck towards Ath Luain,
and onwards to Roscomain and the great, green
bird-haunted plain of Moy-Lurg; and leaving it
behind him he went over the blue Curlew Hills,
with the bloom of the grape lying on them, and
so to the mountain of Kesh-Corran; and from
there looked down to the Great Plain of the
Assembly where the Fomorians lay encamped.

So as he drew near to the camp, clad in his battle
clothing and riding the mare Enbarr, Bres, son of
Balor called the druids and other wise men of the
host to him and said, "Great wonders may be
expected on this day, for the light of the sun has
risen up in the west."

"Better would it be for us all if that were so,"
said the druids, "but evil and dark is the portent."

"And how do you explain that?" asked Bres.

"It is no uneasy riddle," they answered, "for
the light you see is a reflection from the fair-
seeming countenance of Lugh the Long-Handed,

25

and from the flashing of his sharp-edged deadly weapons—and he it was who slew the tax gatherers."

And hardly were the words spoken when Lugh rode quietly into the midst of the host, and gave them peaceful and courteous greeting.

Then one of the company spoke out and said to Lugh, "How comes it that you salute us in this manner, since we know you to be our enemy?"

And Lugh answered, "It is true that I have cause for dispute with you, but I salute you because only half the blood in my veins is of the De Danann—and the other half was given me by your own kin, for I am son to your king's daughter Ethlenn. I am come among you in peace if you will have it so—to ask if you will give back to the men of Connacht that which you have stolen from them."

"May evil be your portion this day," cried one of the Fomorians, "and not one milch cow will you get from us."

And the others raised their voices loudly in agreement.

Then Lugh smiled coldly on the hosts from Lochlann—and he lifted his left hand and moved it twice in the air—and in this wise he put a magic spell on the stolen cattle, so that each one of the milch cows went back without being driven to her owner's door; but the dry cattle he left with the Fomorians to be a burden to them, and to hinder their movements. And this he did that they might be forced to stay in that place until the Fairy Host should come to do battle with them.

Thus for three days and for three long dark nights Lugh remained near the camp of the Fomorians; and on the fourth day, when the first dazzling shaft of sunlight struck across the plain from the eastern horizon, the Fairy Host were seen approaching. And not long after they had encamped themselves near the Fomorians, Bove Derg, son of Dagda, rode up with two thousand of the warriors and chieftains of Connacht, and Bove Derg made peace with Lugh the Long-Handed—and so they made ready for the fight.

Now Lugh hastened to array himself in his splendid war apparel; he put on Mannanan's coat of mail, and his breast-plate; and he took his helmet called Cathbharr, which flashed so brilliantly in the sun that fifty men of the Fomorians were struck blind by its piercing rays. He slung his dark-blue glittering shield upon his shoulder, and his sword Answerer hung by his side; and in his hands he held his two long, heavy-shafted spears, whose prick was as deadly as the venom of adders.

Then the other kings and nobles of Erin gathered their men together, and placed them cunningly in battle ranks; soon their spears rose like the spines of a hedgehog high over their heads—and their great, gold-studded shields were placed edge to edge to form a firm, impenetrable fence around them. So they awaited the signal to launch themselves against their foes—and the Fomorians, undaunted, awaited their onset in silence.

Suddenly a fierce, ringing shout rose into the heavens, and echoed like a bronze bell across the plain—and with this cry, the Fairy Host and the men of Connacht surged forward like a mighty wave of the ocean and fell upon the enemy.

At once a black cloud of whizzing javelins darkened the skies, flying from line to line across the space between the contending hosts, and as the first warriors rushed forward to attack, their spears quivered in their hands, and sent out rays of light like sunlight on moving waters. Then, as they came together in conflict, the warriors drew their gold-hilted swords, and so they fought foot to foot, with upraised shields, and fierce sharp cries—and the plain was filled with the clashing of weapons and the crashing of shield on shield, and the sorrowful moans of the wounded and dying.

And wherever the fighting was thickest, there was found Lugh the Long-Handed—and so strong and deadly was his onslaught that the dead rose in piles around him, and the stroke of his sword was more to be dreaded than lightning.

Now in the midst of the fight Lugh looked around him, and seeing Bres, son of Balor, with a company of his Fomorians dealing havoc and terror among the Tuatha De Danann, he cut his way through the press between them, and attacked Bres's bodyguard with such fury that in a few moments he had slain them to a man. Then he

fell upon Bres, and dealt him a cruel stroke on the
helm with his sword the Answerer; and Bres,
unable to stand against his onset, cried out, "Why
must we be enemies, O Lugh, since you are of
my kin? Let there be a truce between us, for I
cannot withstand thy blows."

When Lugh heard these words he stayed his
hand, and asked Bres what conditions he would
agree to for the sake of peace.

Then Bres cried, "I will undertake never again to fight against thee—let there be peace between us." And he swore by the sun and moon, and by all the elements to keep his promise—and so Lugh granted him his life.

Now when the men of Lochlann saw their chief vanquished, their hearts failed them, and they had no further wish to continue the fight. And in no long time the druids and men of learning among them came to Lugh and asked him to spare their lives. And Lugh answered and said, "It is no wish of mine to destroy you, nor did I start this slaughter. Let you take your people now, and return to your own lands and leave us in peace." And this they agreed to do.

And so the Fomorians departed out of Erin for that time, and Lugh and the Fairy Host rested from the turmoil and heat of battle.

4. Lugh and his Father's Murderers

NOW LUGH the Long-Handed had noticed that his father had not come to join him for the battle with the Fomorians, and when all was settled, he went to two of his friends and asked them if they had seen Kian at all—and they answered, "No". Then Lugh was greatly troubled, and said to them, "Certain it is that my father is dead, or a prisoner, for had he been alive and free he would have come to help me in the fight. So I swear neither to rest nor eat until I have found out where his body lies, and who has slain him, for I am sure it was done by treachery."

After that Lugh chose a small band of trusty warriors from among the Fairy Host, and they set out, and travelled on the pure, cold crimson wind until they came to the place where Lugh had parted from his father. And from there they went southwards to the plain of Murthemna where Kian had encountered the Sons of Tuireann.

And when they had been searching for a while, it chanced that Lugh came near to the place where his father was buried—and he was a little ahead of his companions. And suddenly the earth moved under his feet, and the stones of the earth spoke, and they said, "Thy father lies here, O Lugh; grievous was his strait, for he was forced to take the shape of a pig to escape from the Children of Tuireann. But they caught him, and slew him in his own shape—and this deed shall darken their lives till their doom be fulfilled."

Then Lugh spoke, and he said, "A merciless and wicked death has my beloved father suffered at the hands of the Sons of Tuireann. Woeful indeed is this day to me—for the light of the sun is darkened in my sight, and I can no longer hear the sweet songs of birds in my ears, or join in laughter or happiness while my heart is numbed with sorrow. For evil is this deed done by kinsmen against kinsman—and vengeance shall follow these murderers until they too find an end in death."

Then they dug another grave, and placed Kian in it, and they raised a great pillar of stone over it, and carved his name in ogham upon it; and after that they sang the lays of lamentation and remembrance, and the funeral games were performed, and so the rites were ended.

When this had been done, Lugh turned to his companions, and said to them, "It is my wish now that ye go with all speed to Tara, where the king of Erin sits among the Tuatha De Danann. But speak no word of the death of Kian my father, or make it known abroad until I come to join you."

So they went straightway to Tara.

Now we do not know where Lugh went, or how

he fared until he came to Tara, and was met with great honour, for the king of Erin put him in a place high above all others, and that was by his own side; for the fame of Lugh's deeds had gone over the whole land, and he was acclaimed a mighty hero.

When Lugh had seated himself in his great carven chair, he looked about him, and soon enough his gaze fell upon the Sons of Tuireann among the assembly of princes and warriors—for these young men were noted champions, exceeding all others in form and comeliness, in feats of valour and skill, and their renown was nearly as great as that of Lugh himself.

Howsoever, Lugh turned to Nuada the king, and requested him to let the chain of silence be shaken, this being a chain hung about with small golden bells which was rung when the lord of the house wished to gain the attention of the company. And when all were ready to hear him, he stood up, and spoke thus: "Seeing that ye are of a mind to give me a hearing, O ye princes and nobles of the De Danann race, I would put a question to each one of you: what vengeance would you take of the man who should kill your father of treacherous and evil intent?"

Then all present were filled with amazement, and the king of Erin, Nuada of the Silver Hand, said to Lugh, "What mean you, O Lugh? For your father is still living at this hour."

But Lugh stood silent for a while, and when at

33

last men began to murmur among themselves and
there was an uneasy stir in the hall, he said loudly,
"My father is dead, O Nuada, and moreover those
who slew him are here in this place. And the
manner of the slaying is known to me, as it is
known in their hearts."

At this, a confused clamour broke out among
the assembly, but the Sons of Tuireann by common consent said nothing; and so the king spoke,
and he said, "If any man did such evil to my
father I would see that he died in torment—for
no pain could be enough to atone for the deed."

And all the company gave assent to his words,
and the Sons of Tuireann with them.

Then Lugh the Long-Handed spoke again, and
he said, "Those guilty men who caused my father's
death are in this hall and have given their assent
with the rest to the judgment of the king of Erin.
Therefore, I call upon all the Tuatha De Danann
to witness that I claim eric-fine for the death of
my father. It is not my intention to violate the
king's law of protection, but it is certain that those
men shall not go out from Mi Corta until this
matter is settled."

At these words, Nuada said, "Fortunate indeed
are they that you should claim no more from them
than eric-fine."

Then the Children of Tuireann murmured
among themselves; and at last Iuchar spoke out:
"O Nuada, and all here assembled, it is of us that
Lugh the Long-Handed speaks; and better it is

that we should acknowledge our guilt, for it avails us nothing to hide it."

And Brian raised his voice and said, "It is known to all that we have long been at enmity with the Sons of Canta—so our word would not be believed if we denied the slaying of Kian. Therefore we are willing to pay the eric for him—and let us know what it is to be."

Then Lugh spoke: "I shall name the eric now, taking all here assembled to witness what I ask. The first part is three apples; the second, the skin of a pig; the third is a spear; the fourth, two horses and a chariot; the fifth, seven pigs; the sixth, a hound-whelp; the seventh, a cooking-spit; and the eighth, three loud cheers on a high hill. If ye think it too much, say so now—or agree to pay all."

"It is not too great for us so far," said Brian, "but we fear some hidden mischief in your words."

"Well then," said Lugh, "I pledge myself before these witnesses to ask no more of you, nor to exact further vengeance for my father's death. But I demand your given word to be faithful in payment of the eric."

"Ill is it that you should doubt our pledged word, seeing that we three Sons of Tuireann are not unknown in Erin," cried the three brothers together.

"I have known great warriors fail in their promises before now, even though they gave assent before many witnesses," said Lugh.

Then the Sons of Tuireann consented to bind

themselves before all the people—and so both sides made their promises, and Nuada the king of Erin, and Bove Derg, son of Dagda, and all the princes and nobles of the De Dananns were witnesses and sureties of the bond.

Then Lugh raised his voice, and said, "Now it is fitting that I should give you the full knowledge of this eric-fine. I ask for three apples of Hisberna, far to the east of the world, and hard you will find it to take them from under the eyes of their guardians.

"And I demand the skin of the pig of Tuis, king of Greece; and the venomous spear of Pezar, king of Persia, the name of which is the Slaughterer.

"Moreover I ask from you the horses and chariot of Dobhar king of Sigar, and the seven pigs of Asal, king of the Golden Pillars.

"I must have the king of Iroda's hound-whelp Falinis, which shines so brightly that all wild beasts fall dead before him.

"The cooking-spit belongs to the fierce women of the island of Fincara, who are thrice fifty in number, and have never been vanquished in combat.

"And the hill on which I require that ye give three loud shouts is the Hill of Midkena in the north of Lochlann, for Midkena and his sons keep a perpetual watch on that hill, for they are under geasa not to let any man shout upon it. Moreover, they it was who instructed my father in all knightly

feats of arms, and he was dear to their hearts—
and even if I should forgive you his death ye may
be certain they would not.

"This, Sons of Tuireann, is the eric-fine I demand of you."

When the Children of Tuireann heard the terms
of the eric they were sorely cast down and dismayed, so that without further words they rose,
and left the king's hall of Mi Corta, and returned
in haste to their father's house.

5. The Golden Apples of Hisberna

Now WHEN the Sons of Tuireann had told their father about the slaying of Kian, and the eric-fine they had agreed to pay, he said, "Ill tidings are these, my sons, but the judgment is a just one, for it was an evil deed to kill Kian in such wise. Greatly do I fear that you will find your deaths in your payment of the eric—so I counsel you to ask for help from Lugh the Long-Handed. Go now to him, and ask for the loan of his horse, Enbarr—and if he will not give you your desire, ask again for Mannanan's canoe the Wave-Sweeper. One request he may refuse, but he is forbidden to refuse the second."

So the Children of Tuireann went to Lugh, and after greetings had been exchanged, they said, "It is not in our power to fulfil all the terms of the eric, O Lugh, unless you are willing to aid us: so we have come to ask for the loan of Mannanan's horse, Enbarr of the Flowing Mane."

"Sorry am I to refuse your request," answered Lugh, "but well ye know that the horse is not mine own, but is only lent to me, and so I cannot lend it again."

"That being so," said Brian, "we pray you to aid us by the loan of the canoe the Wave-Sweeper."

"That I can lend you," said Lugh, "and ye will find it lying at Brugh on the Boyne."

So they thanked Lugh for his aid, and went back to their father, and told him of the success of their mission. And their father said, "It seems to me that Lugh is willing to help you with those parts of the eric which may be most useful to himself— but when ye come to seek what cannot advantage him, namely the cooking-spit, and the three loud shouts on the Hill of Midkena, he will be glad to see you perish in the attempt."

Then the three brothers hastened to Brugh on the Boyne, and saw there the canoe of Mannanan, which had the magic property of being able to enlarge itself to accommodate all who desired to sit in it. And they took their arms and their war clothing, and entered the canoe, and rowed hard until they had left behind the fair, safe harbours of Erin, and were launched on to the deep waters of the ocean.

Then Iucharba said to his brothers, "How shall we know what direction to take, or how to set our course?"

And Brian said, "Let us ask the canoe to take us swiftly to the Garden of Hisberna, for the apples are the first part of our quest."

So he spoke to the Wave-Sweeper, and when the canoe heard his command, it leapt forward with the strength and speed of a salmon, and cutting a smooth path through the white-tipped green-blue waves, it stayed not until it reached the land of Hisberna.

Then the brothers bade it find a small, smooth harbour, and this it did, and they tied the canoe securely to the mooring-posts and began to discuss among themselves the best way to set about obtaining the apples.

Now the apples of Hisberna were famed throughout all the world, for there were no others like them for beauty or virtue. They were as burnished gold in appearance, and their flavour was sweet and delicate beyond imagining—moreover, they were never made smaller by eating. If any wounded man, or one smitten by sickness ate of them, he was cured in that instant. Also, if a champion wished to perform a feat of skill, and cast the apple at a mark, it would return of itself into his hand. And it had been foretold in past times that a day would come when three young heroes of the Island of the West would take the apples by force, so that the king of Hisberna had set a perpetual watch on them by day and night.

All this the Sons of Tuireann knew—and so now they decided to change themselves into three strong, swift hawks and swoop down upon the trees from a great height, thus taking the guards by surprise. And when this was done, the three slender, beautiful birds flew as swiftly as the clear, cold blue wind of March, and began to descend in great sweeping circles towards the tree-tops. But the vigilant watchers perceived them even when they were very high up, and with loud shouts and cries of alarm threw showers of sharp, deadly darts at them. Howsoever these the hawks escaped, for Brian had warned his brothers to be wary of them.

Then, when the guards had used all their weapons, the hawks swooped down so speedily that the eye could not follow their flight, and the two younger brothers each carried off an apple in his beak, while Brian held two, one in his beak and another between his talons; and the three birds rose up into the air without receiving any wound or hurt, and flew out over the sea towards the west.

Quickly the news was carried to the chief city of Hisberna that three hawks had carried away the golden apples—and there were loud lamentations and cries of anger from the people, and the king was consumed with wrath.

Now there were three princesses, daughters of the king; and they were skilled in all magical arts, and in wise counsel; and when they had spoken with their father, they hastened to change themselves into three strong-winged, sharp-clawed griffins—and so they sped forth like arrows in pursuit of the hawks.

But when the hawks saw them coming, they increased their speed, and flew faster than the winds, so that the griffins fell far behind, and could hardly

41

perceive their prey, so small were they against the vastness of the sky.

Then the griffins opened wide their beaks, and sent forth fierce, crimson flashes of fire which reached the hawks, and scorched their feathers, and half-blinded them with heat. And the two younger brothers said to Brian, "Terrible is our state now, for we can no longer endure these burning flames; tell us what to do before we perish."

"Have no fears, for it is in my power to save you," said Brian, and in an instant, by the aid of his magic virtues he had transformed himself and his brothers into snow-white proud swans. Without a moment's delay the swans dropped down upon the waters of the sea, and the griffins, unable any longer to see the hawks fleeing before them, gave up the chase and turned homewards.

Then the Sons of Tuireann flew swiftly to their canoe, and resumed their proper shapes, and unloosing the mooring ropes, they sailed speedily out of the harbour and left the shores of Hisberna far behind them, turning their prow to the West.

And so they were successful in their first venture.

6. The Gifted Skin of the Pig

NOW AFTER they had sailed for a time on tranquil seas, and refreshed themselves with the cool, sharp-tasting salty air, the Sons of Tuireann held

council together—for it was necessary to decide what next to do. And in the end they resolved to make their way to Greece, and there obtain the skin of the pig demanded by Lugh as part of the eric-fine.

It was known to all that the king of Greece was determined that no strangers should steal away the skin. For when the pig had been alive, every stream of water she went into had been turned into wine for a period of nine days—and all who had suffered any wound or sickness had only to touch her skin to be healed. Now king Tuis sent for his wise men, and asked them how the life of the pig might be preserved—and they answered him, and said that this was not necessary, for the virtue of the pig lay in her skin. And when the king heard these words, he had the pig killed instantly, and then she was skinned, and he kept the skin, and it was regarded as a great treasure.

So it was that as the canoe swept lightly over the waves the Sons of Tuireann began to talk together about the way to gain footing at the Greek king's court. Iuchar thought that they should go in their own shape, as three bold champions out of the West. Iucharba waited to hear what the others would say. At last Brian spoke out, and he said, "You will know that poets are held in great honour among the princes and nobles of Greece—and it seems to me that we should say we are three learned poets from Erin, for in that manner no one will suspect our real purpose."

Then the others cried out in dismay, and said that they knew no poems, and would not know how to compose one—but Brian told them to leave the talking to him and all would be well, and so it was settled.

So when the canoe brought them to shore close to the palace of the king, they all three tied up their hair in the manner of poets, and presented themselves at the door of the palace. And when the doorkeeper opened to them, and asked their names, and why they had come, Brian said that they were learned ferdana, poets out of Erin, bringing a new poem in honour of the king of Greece. The man went straightway to king Tuis, and repeated the message, and the king said, "Let them enter, for they come to seek one in whom the love of learning is known to be found—and it is a long way from Erin to Greece."

So the Sons of Tuireann were brought into the great banqueting hall, hung around with brightly-coloured embroidered cloths, and having vessels of gold and silver on the long table, and finely chased and gilded drinking cups; and here the king sat, with his princes and nobles around him.

At once the Sons of Tuireann were made welcome, and invited to sit at table and join in the feasting, and never had they seen such splendour, or so great a company assembled under one roof.

Soon enough it was time for the king's poets to rise and recite their poems, as was the custom at that court—and many fine lays were heard, and splendid and lofty words echoed round the hall, and loud was the applause for them all. And as was to be expected, the visitors were called on to speak, and to recite the poem they had composed in honour of the king; and Iuchar and Iucharba looked at each other in dismay and foreboding.

But Brian rose up from his seat near the king, and turning towards him he said:

> "It is to praise thee, O Tuis, that we are come,
> Loud shall be our praise,
> For thou hast gladdened many hearts in this
>   land
> With thy bounty and keen-bright love of
>   learning.
>
> It is not good for neighbours to come to blows,
> A poet unrequited is a dreadful enemy,
> Let the king's bounty add to his fame,
> And now the Imnocta-fessa I claim."

"Your poem would doubtless be thought a good one in Erin," said Tuis, "but we cannot judge of it, for it is unlike all other poems we have heard, and some lines are hard to be understood."

"I will give you the sense of it," said Brian. "The first verse is not difficult, and the meaning of the second is this—I ask for the skin of the pig as a reward for the poem, for 'imnocta' is skin, and 'fessa' a pig in our tongue. And the second line means that if you will not give it to me, I will take it from you by force—and that, O king, is the sense of my poem."

"I thank you for your poem, O ferdana," said Tuis, "and it would please me greatly if you had not spoken of a pig's skin, for that is but a foolish request, seeing that it is known all over the world

46

that I will not part with the skin. So accept from me the full of the skin in red-gold, and let us hear no more of the matter."

"That is a good and fair sum, O Tuis," said Brian, "but I am known to be a suspicious man, and I ask that I may be present when the gold is measured."

So Tuis agreed to this request, and he sent his servants to fetch the pig's skin and the gold, and they brought it into the hall, and a space was cleared, and two men held the skin open while a third filled it with gold. Suddenly then, Brian sprang forward, and dealt this man a mighty blow which felled him to the floor, and before the other two could defend themselves he snatched the skin from them, and tied it around him. Then he drew his sharp-edged shining sword, and his brothers did likewise—and they rushed upon the king's nobles and warriors, who hastened to defend themselves. But so strong and fierce was the onset of the Sons of Tuireann, that, although they were many times outnumbered, they scattered all their foes and scarce left one unhurt of that great company.

At last Brian and the king of Greece stood face to face—nor was Tuis slow to answer Brian's challenge. So they fought long and hard, being both noted warriors and champions, and each dealt the other many dreadful wounds, so that for a time it was doubtful who should prevail. But after the combat had endured for endless-seeming hours,

47

the king of Greece fell dead, overcome by the valour of Brian son of Tuireann.

And so they were successful in their second venture, and rested in the palace for a while, healing their grievous wounds by means of the golden apples of Hisberna and the pig's skin. But there were still many hazards before them.

7. The Spear Slaughterer and the Chariot and Horses of Sigar

WHEN THREE whole days and nights had passed, the Sons of Tuireann held counsel together, and it was decided that they should set out to find the blazing spear of the king of Persia.

Then Iucharba said to his brothers, "There is no doubt that we shall be able to make our way to Persia with the aid of the Wave-Sweeper and our own skills—but how shall we bring back the spear without hurt to ourselves?" And this he said because the spear of Pezar was famed all over the known world—for not only was the blade full of deadly venom, from which no one wounded by it might recover, but also a perpetual, fiery flame sprang from it, so that the head of the spear had to be kept in a great cauldron of icy water lest it set fire to the king's palace. And this water had to be changed every hour, for the heat of the blade soon made it boil and seethe, and fill the air with thick, evil-smelling smoke.

But Brian as ever was undaunted, and replied, "Have we not carried off the golden apples of

49

Hisberna, and the pig's skin of the king of Greece, and are we any the worse for it? Let us go to Persia, and when we are there we will think of a plan."

And to this Iuchar and Iucharba gave their assent.

Now they sailed away from the blue, smiling seas of Greece, and crossed over wide and stormy waters, and we do not know how long it took them to reach the land of Persia—but certain it is that one day they found themselves outside the palace of the king, and with no better plan than to say again that they were poets from Erin. And when they were brought before the king that was what they did—and so all went as it had done at the court of Greece, save that when Brian rose to recite his poem, he altered the words "imnoctafessa," and said "flaming javelin".

"I am satisfied with your poem," said the king of Persia, "but I cannot understand why you make mention of a flaming javelin."

"Well," said Brian, "it is because I wish to ask for your spear the Slaughterer as a reward for the poem."

"That is indeed an unwise request," said the king, "and the only reward I may offer you now is to ask my nobles and warriors to let you go from here without harm—for it is my custom to put to death instantly anyone who asks me for my spear."

Then Brian made a small sign to his brothers, and they sprang up, and drew their swords out of the scabbards, and the king and his nobles did likewise; and soon the great hall echoed with fierce shouts, and the sound of steel hissing against steel, and so the fight raged up and down for many long hours. But suddenly Brian remembered all he had heard of the apples of Hisberna, and taking one of the two he carried secretly on his person, he flung it with great force at Pezar king of Persia, so that it cracked his skull, and he fell dead to the floor.

After this the three Sons of Tuireann fought with renewed vigour, and terrible were their blows —so that the nobles and chieftains of Persia, losing heart at last because of the death of their king, broke and fled out of the hall leaving Brian and his brothers the victors.

Now as soon as their enemies had departed, the Sons of Tuireann went with all speed to the room where the flaming spear was kept—and as they entered they were nearly blinded by steam, and their mouths and noses were filled with the evil-smelling vapour; and their hearts were shaken by the roaring sound made by the water in the huge cauldron, as it bubbled and foamed, throwing great jets of boiling water into the air.

But at last Brian took courage, and wrapping his cloak round his hand and arm, he walked boldly up to the cauldron, and drew forth the spear by the shaft—and so, holding it with the head held out in front of him he turned and left that place—and his brothers followed him, and so we hear no more of them for a while.

Howsoever, there comes a day when we hear of the Sons of Tuireann sailing smoothly and lightly over the green-blue waves of the sea, resolved to seek Sigar and capture the horses and chariot of the king, which had been named as the fourth part of the eric-fine.

And when they had reached the island's chief harbour, they discussed among themselves how best to carry out their intention.

Iuchar and Iucharba thought that they should go in their own guise as three famous champions of Erin, come to get the horses and chariot by peaceful means, or if necessary, by force. But to this Brian would not agree.

"My counsel is that we say we are warriors from Erin wishing to be taken into the king's service," said he, "and by that means we shall quickly find out where the chariot and horses are kept."

And as his brothers had no better plan they agreed to do this, and set out for the palace.

Now on that day the king was holding a great assembly on the broad green grass before the palace, and when the three strangers were seen approaching, people stood aside to let them pass, and so they came to the king, and bowed low before him; and he asked their names, and the reason of their coming.

Then they answered all together, "We are soldiers out of Erin, and we heard your name being spoken of as that of one of the great kings of the world, and so we are here to seek service with you."

Then the king answered and said he would be willing to make a covenant with them, and they asked to be placed in a post of honour and trust; and he agreed to do this, and they on their part promised to give him faithful service, and it was agreed that they might name their own reward.

So three weeks went by and the brothers remained at the palace and performed those duties to which they were appointed—but in all that time they neither saw nor heard anything of the king's horses and chariot.

Now it was said of these horses that there were none to equal them for strength and swiftness, and that they could travel by sea as well as by land. And the chariot was of such beauty of form and colour that there was none other like it. The body of the chariot was of a deep, rich-seeming green, and the wheels were made of red-gold, with an inlay of enamel, and a setting of precious jewels at the centre—and all men envied the king of Sigar for possessing such a treasure.

When another two weeks had gone by, Iuchar and Iucharba asked Brian what they should do in the matter. And he answered them, "It seems to me that we should put on our travelling clothes, and take up our weapons of valour, and say to the king that unless he will grant us a sight of his horses and chariot we will leave his service."

Then the brothers said to Brian, "Let you do

the talking," and to this he agreed—and so they went to the king with their request. When the king saw them arrayed as for a journey with their weapons in their hands, he asked why they came to him thus. And Brian said, "We have travelled in many strange lands, O king, and wheresoever we have gone we have been trusted by the kings and nobles of that country, and shown all their rare treasures and gifted arms of victory—yet you, O king, possess a chariot and two horses unlike any others in the world, but never once have you offered to let us see them—and so we ask leave to depart from your court."

"This is a great ado ye make about a small matter," said the king, "for how was I to know that you wished to see my chariot and horses when you said no word to me? And ye have no need to leave my service, for if that is all ye ask from me, ye shall have your wish within the hour."

Then he sent a messenger to the stables, and ordered the horses to be yoked to the chariot, and to be brought to the door of the palace—and it was done.

The Sons of Tuireann were loud in their praise of the night-black slender steeds, and the shining green chariot, and Brian said to the king, "Hear us, O king. We thank you for granting our request so speedily, and now we would ask you for our reward for the faithful service we have performed. And the reward we ask is the gift of your chariot and horses—and there is nothing other that will suffice."

Then the king was filled with fury, and he said to them, "Never will I grant your foolish request —and you will certainly die because of it."

With these words he took up his sword, and his warriors likewise, and sprang upon the Sons of Tuireann to make an end of them. But they were not taken by surprise and defended themselves with skill and valour. And when an opportunity arose Brian suddenly leapt into the chariot, and slew the charioteer with one stroke, and seized up the reins in his left hand; then, raising the flaming spear of Pezar he made a fierce thrust at the king of Sigar, and the envenomed point struck through his breast, and came out at his back—and he fell dead. And the Children of Tuireann fought with great strength and courage, and dealt destruction and terror among the remaining warriors, so that they fled in all directions. And so they were successful in their fourth venture.

8. The Seven Enchanted Pigs, and the Hound-whelp of Iroda

AFTER TIME enough had passed for the Sons of Tuireann to recover from the hurts they had received in their encounter with the warriors of Sigar, they decided among themselves to go next to Asal, king of the Golden Pillars, and ask for the gift of his seven pigs. And the brothers were resolved on this occasion to go to him in their own shapes and speak truth, and see what would come of it.

So they entered their canoe the Wave-Sweeper, and told it where they wished to go; and we do not know how they fared until they reached the land of the Golden Pillars, save that they arrived in good health, and with a firm intention to abide by their plan.

Now as the canoe drew near to the shore, they saw a great company of armed men waiting for them at the landing-place; for the noise of their former deeds had gone into many lands; and it was known that by reason of the eric-fine demanded by the Ildana Lugh they had been forced to leave Erin; and moreover, men had heard that they were going to and fro in the world, and snatching away by force many famous and rare treasures—so that Asal, king of the Golden Pillars, had ordered a watch to be set on his coasts, and any strangers were to be prevented from landing.

When the news of their arrival was sent to the palace, the king himself came down to the harbour, and when they were near enough to hear his words, he ordered them to stay their sailing; and in threatening tones asked them why they were come to his lands, and if they were the heroes of Erin who had slain so many of the great kings of the world.

Then Brian stood up in the canoe, and answered Asal thus: "Let you know, O king, that we are indeed the three Sons of Tuireann, and it seems to us that you have heard how we were forced to leave our country because of the Ildana's demands. Nor can we be blamed that we took those treasures we sought by force—for we offered to take them peaceably—and were roughly refused. We have given our promise to fulfil all that is asked of us to pay the eric-fine, and the Tuatha De Danann are witness to this—so we may not fail. And so we are come to ask you to give us your seven pigs, for they are a part of the bargain."

Then Asal replied, "And if I refuse your request, what will ye do?"

And Brian said, "You must know, O Asal, that if we do not pay the fine we shall suffer death at

57

the hands of our people. Therefore we ask you to take pity on our plight, and help us out of friendship. But if you refuse, then must we get the pigs by force, and either slay many in the attempt, or die ourselves."

When the king heard these words, he held a council with his wise men and the chiefs of the people, and they decided to give the pigs to the Sons of Tuireann without further argument, for so far no one had been able to stand against them in combat.

So word was taken to the Children of Tuireann, and they were invited to land and to rest from their journeyings. And they were given a kindly welcome, and food and drink, and that night they had soft beds to sleep on—and so they had ease for the first time since they started on their quest.

And when morning came they were brought before the king; and the pigs were given to them; and Asal said, "Sorely does it grieve me to part with these pigs, for any who eats of them suffers no sickness or hurt, and if you were to eat one today, and put the bones together in a heap afterwards, you would find that pig whole on the morrow. But sorry am I for your plight, nor do we wish to fight with you and perchance be slain —so ye may take them, and go in peace and safety."

Then Brian and his brothers thanked the king with lightness in their hearts and Brian said, "O Asal, in days to come many famous poets shall sing of this deed, and your name shall be honoured for ever in green Erin—for never shall we forget how you offered us your friendship freely and without anger. And now we wish you good health and long days . . ." And so he ended.

Then Asal answered him, and thanked him for his words, and the king said, "Tell me, O Son of Tuireann, whither does your quest lead you now?"

"We must hasten to Iroda to gain possession of the king's hound-whelp Falinis," replied Brian.

"It is no wonder to me that Lugh the Long-Handed should wish to have this beast for his own," said the king, "but I ask a request of you in my turn, and that is that you let me go with you to Iroda; for my daughter is wife to the king, and so it might be that I could prevail on him to give you the hound without battle."

This the Sons of Tuireann gladly agreed to, and it was settled that Asal should take them in his own ship. So when all was prepared for their coming they went on board, taking all their treasures with them—and we know nothing more until they reached Iroda.

When they sailed near to the land they saw that all the shore was lined by bands of fierce-seeming, valiant warriors, and these men shouted loudly that they were there by the king's command, and the ship must let drop her anchors and venture no closer; for well they knew that the Sons of Tuireann were on her, and why they were come to Iroda.

Then Asal said to the Sons of Tuireann that it were best if he left them in the ship, and went alone to speak with his son-in-law, and so it was settled. And the warriors let Asal land, and they took him to the king who gave him a gentle greeting. But when they had conversed for a time, the king of Iroda asked why Asal had come with the Sons of Tuireann—and Asal said, "I am here to ask you to give them your hound-whelp Falinis, that there may be no bloodshed this day."

Then the king of Iroda answered him in anger, saying, "Ill advice have you given these men, for there is no hero in the world who shall take my hound-whelp from me, and this you may tell them."

"You will suffer great evil if you refuse their request," said Asal; and he told his son-in-law of all the kings and warriors who had been slain by the Sons of Tuireann. But his words of warning availed nothing, for the king of Iroda waxed even more wrathful, and refused to hear any more of the matter. So Asal returned to the Sons of Tuireann and told them all that had happened.

Then the Sons of Tuireann were angered in their turn, and they put on their clothing of combat and valour, and took up their weapons in their hands, and prepared to do battle without further delay. And so it was that a long and dreadful fight was begun—for the warriors of Iroda were many and full of lofty courage, and so they fought bravely, and so well did they withstand the on-

60

slaught of the Sons of Tuireann that Brian became separated from his two brothers, and was altogether surrounded by his foes. When he saw his own danger, he snatched up the spear of Pezar, and turned its fierce, flaming point against those who opposed him—and it was not long before all the men of Iroda fell away before him, leaving a wide path between themselves and the fearsome weapon.

It was then that Brian saw the king of Iroda standing encircled by a hedge of spears; and at once the Son of Tuireann rushed to that place, striking furiously around him, and dealing death and terror on all sides as he went. Then Brian put down the spear Slaughterer, and drew his sharp-edged cunning sword, and the two great warriors fought shield to shield until the air around them quivered from the heat of their blows, and sparks flew from the steel like stars falling from the heavens.

Yet in all that time it was in Brian's mind not to slay the king, because he was son-in-law to Asal. And so when he had held back in the combat until he had tired out his foe, he drew suddenly very close to him, and dropping his sword, seized the king in his mighty, iron-gripping arms, and holding him fast bore him to where Asal was standing. Then, setting him on his feet, he said to Asal, "Here is your daughter's husband unhurt—and easily could I have slain him had I so wished. But I remembered your kindness to us, and so I bring him to you—but let you counsel him to offend me no further."

When the king's men saw that he was taken prisoner they abandoned the fight, and prevailed upon him to give the hound-whelp to the Sons of Tuireann, for sore had been their losses that day, and they had no heart for further combat. And so it was done.

And soon after the Sons of Tuireann took their leave of the king of Iroda, and they returned into the ship with Asal and so set sail once more for the land of the Golden Pillars. But they would not rest there many days, in spite of the hospitality offered them; and so it was that they departed, watched by Asal and his nobles and people—and the Wave-Sweeper swiftly bore them over the distant horizon into the mists of the future, and that land saw them no more.

9. The Children of Tuireann Return to Erin

IT IS now time to speak of Lugh the Long-Handed, and see how he fares and what he is doing while the Sons of Tuireann fulfil the sentence he set upon them.

Now through his magical powers Lugh had knowledge of all that was done by the Sons of Tuireann, and he knew that they had obtained all that part of the eric-fine which he required for his own purposes. So he sent a spell after them when they had left the land of the Golden Pillars, and this spell, travelling to them with the speed of the black north wind, shrouded their thoughts in a mist, so that a cloud of oblivion fell on them; and so they forgot that there were still two parts of the eric unfulfilled, and only remembered their homeland; and a great longing seized them to see green Erin again, and they straightway commanded their canoe the Wave-Sweeper to carry them swiftly to their native shores.

At that time Lugh had gone to be with the king of Erin at a great fair-meeting which was to be held on the broad plain of Tara; and while he was there he was told in a dream that the Sons of

Tuireann had landed at Brugh on the Boyne. When he awoke, he left the gathering secretly, and went with all speed to Caher-Crofinn, the chief fortress of Tara, and after closing all the doors behind him, he went within, and began to array himself in his battle clothing; and he put upon himself the cunning Greek armour given him by Mannanan Mac Lir, and over it he wore the enchanted black cloak of the daughter of Flidas.

Soon enough it was noised abroad that the Sons of Tuireann were approaching, and a great crowd of people went out to meet them and give them welcome; and loud were the cries of wonder and admiration when it was seen what rare-seeming treasures they had brought with them.

When the three heroes were come to where Nuada, king of Erin, sat among his nobles and warriors, they were greeted with a joyful welcome by all, and the king asked them how they had fared, and if they had been successful in their quest.

"We have obtained all that was asked of us by the Ildana Lugh," they replied, "and now we wish to give him the eric, and so be free to depart to our father's halls."

Then Nuada told them that Lugh was present at the assembly—but when messengers were sent to fetch him he could not be found, and no one had seen him that day.

When the messengers returned to the king with these tidings Brian spoke, and he said, "It is

64

certain that Lugh has had a foretelling of our coming, and knows that we are even now in this place. And it seems to me that he fears us because we carry the blazing spear of Pezar, and the apples of Hisberna, and has hidden himself in some stronghold in order to avoid us."

Then the king of Erin sent other messengers to the strongholds of Tara, and at last they came to Caher-Crofinn, and found Lugh there, and gave him the tidings that the Sons of Tuireann were returned, and wished to be quit of the eric-fine. But Lugh the Long-Handed refused to accompany them to the plain of Tara, and he said, "Go back, and tell the Sons of Tuireann that I am not yet ready to come to the meeting, but I ask them to give the tribute to the king of Erin in my stead."

So the messengers returned to the king of Erin, and when he had heard them he ordered the Sons of Tuireann to give the fine into his keeping, and this they did—and so Nuada had all the wonderful gifts put in a safe place, and set a strong guard on them; but the Sons of Tuireann kept their own war weapons in their hands, nor would they lay aside their battle clothing—and so all the company went into the palace.

Now soon after this Lugh appeared among the gathering of princes and warriors, and Nuada of the Silver Hand commanded that the fine should be brought to Lugh. And when Lugh had looked long and carefully at all in front of him, he said to the Sons of Tuireann, "Ye have indeed brought

E

me a splendid eric for the death of my father—and it is enough to pay for the death of any hero that should be slain while the world endures. But it is not lawful to withhold even a small part of an eric-fine, and I take you to witness, O Nuada and all ye De Dananns, that here I am offered these things in full payment of my eric—namely, three apples, the skin of the pig, the fiery spear, the chariot and horses, the seven pigs of Asal, and the hound-whelp Falinis. But where, O Children of Tuireann, is the cooking-spit of the fierce women of Fincara? Nor have I heard that ye have given the three loud shouts on the Hill of Midkena."

When they heard these words the Sons of Tuireann were overcome by a deathly chill, and all the strength went out of their limbs, and a faintness came upon them. And so there was a dreadful silence in the hall.

Then the Sons of Tuireann rose up in their place, and with ashen faces left the hall, and no man hindered their going. And they returned speedily to their father's house, and told him and their sister Ethnea all that had befallen—and they confessed that they had forgotten a part of the eric-fine, and so they must leave Erin again, and set out for the land of Fincara. And at these tidings there was sore dismay in the house of Tuireann, and Ethnea wept bitterly, for greatly did she fear the outcome of this quest.

And so the Sons of Tuireann rested in their father's hall for a day and a night. And early on the morrow they rose up, and went down to the shore, and stepped on to one of their father's ships —for they no longer had Mannanan's canoe the Wave-Sweeper—and so they set sail, and were swallowed up into the sea mists.

And great dread and foreboding was upon the household of Tuireann from that hour, and the hearts of all were heavy with a dark sorrow.

10. The Cooking-Spit of the Women of Fincara

So THE Sons of Tuireann returned to their wanderings, and sailed from sea to sea, nor is it known to us what storms they encountered, or what perils from sea-robbers and monsters of the deeps; but certain it is that for a whole year they went to and fro, first on one course, then on another, landing here and there, and asking all whom they saw where the island of Fincara lay; but no one could give them help.

At last, when they were near despair, they met with an old, old man, who told them all that he had heard of the island in his boyhood days. And he said that in those days the island was known as Tir-fa-thonn, and that a spell had been cast upon it, which caused it to sink far down below the green restless waves of the sea—and it was said that only once in seven long years did the island rise again to the top of the waters and become visible to the eyes of men.

When the Sons of Tuireann heard this tale, they talked for a while among themselves, and then Brian said, "It seems to me that we should sail out into the broad distant wastes of the ocean, where no land may be seen, and there we will let down our anchors, and I will go down to the bottom of the sea, and seek for the island." And so it was settled.

And when they had sailed for many weeks, they stayed their course amid the surging, wind-swept waters, and set their anchors firmly, and rested in that place. And Brian put on his water clothing, and his beautiful helmet of crystal on his head; so fine was the crystal that a man could see every smallest shell through it. Then, telling his brothers to await his return howsoever long he might remain below, he leapt over the side of the ship, and sank swiftly out of sight.

Down and down, and yet further down he went, until at last his feet rested on the hard, rocky bed of the sea. And without any delay he began his search for the island of Fincara. Many strange and wonderful sights he saw—there were fishes great and small—some painted in brilliant reds, and blues and greens, some flashing silver light, others which had lights inside their bodies which showed all their bones. One huge creature swam past him holding a long sharply-pointed sword in its mouth —and he saw a sea-serpent with green and black scales, whose sinewy, twisting body seemed to stretch far beyond his sight. There were hundreds of beautiful shells, delicate and strange, and richly coloured sea plants which waved their fine, soft fronds to and fro as he passed; and once he found a little clump of deep scarlet flowers—but when he stooped to touch their petals, they suddenly closed themselves into a tight bud.

So, for over two weary weeks he walked about on the bottom of the green, salty sea—and then one day, he saw a dim, purple-seeming shape rise up before him, and when he drew nearer he found it was the island of Fincara.

Then, with great effort and many false beginnings he climbed the steep, slippery rocks of the island, and at last found a path which led him to the top. And when he had rested awhile, and looked about him, he saw that there were many houses scattered here and there, but one among them was larger than the rest. So he went cautiously towards the door, and when he came near to it, he saw that it stood open.

Then he took courage, and entering, he found himself in a wide and lofty hall, hung with silks of blue and green with rich, strange-seeming figures woven on them. And sitting round a table was a great company of beautiful women, all busied with needlework and many sorts of embroidery; and in the centre of the table stood a long, brightly-shining cooking-spit.

So Brian stood, and looked his fill; and after a little time had passed, he walked boldly forward, and striding up to the table he seized the spit suddenly, and turning went again towards the door.

Now while he had been in the hall none of the women had either moved or spoken—but certain it is that they had all seen him enter, and they were filled with admiration of his splendid form and his manly beauty, and they were also pleased because he had shown no signs of fear.

So when they saw that he was about to escape with the spit in his hand, they all began to laugh —and the sound echoed round the hall like a chiming of silver bells.

And when he turned in surprise, one among them who seemed to be their queen said to him, "This is a bold deed indeed that you have attempted, O Son of Tuireann—for there are thrice fifty valiant, war-like women in this place, and any one among them could have prevented you from taking the spit, even had your brothers been here to give you aid. But because you would not show fear, and were ready to make the attempt, and we know you to be a great hero and a mighty warrior, it is in our hearts to give you this spit, for we have others. So now, take it, and go in peace."

Then Brian gave them gentle thanks and words of praise, and joyfully bearing the spit he left the island, and sought about for his ship.

Now Iuchar and Iucharba had done as he bade them, and remained in one place awaiting his return. But days and weeks went by, and he did not appear, and they were filled with unease, and had begun to fear that he would not come back to them. There came a day when they were almost resolved to take up the anchors and leave the place, when suddenly they saw the flash of Brian's glittering, crystal helmet rising up from the depths, and soon enough his head showed above the clear, ever-moving green waves of the sea.

So he came to the ship, and climbed up her side, and showed them the spit which he had been given by the women of Fincara. And their hearts were filled with joy—and now there was only one venture before them in payment of the eric-fine demanded by Lugh the Long-Handed.

11. The Shouts on the Hill of Midkena

———

Now it seemed to the Sons of Tuireann that their years of toil and hardship were nearly over, and so it was that their hearts were lighter than they had been for many long days as they set their course towards the north, and sailed across the cold, storm-swept waters of the sea towards Lochlann.

Colder it seemed every hour, and mists rose around them, and they heard voices and strange cries, now on one hand, now on the other, and their sails were stiff with ice. But still they sailed on past Lochlann, far up into the Northern waters, until one day they saw the smooth, green Hill of Midkena, rising steeply up above the sea-shore; and so they sailed near to the place, and moored the ship.

Now Midkena had heard of the death of Lugh's father Kian, and sore was his grief at these tidings, and he had sworn to take vengeance on those who had slain Kian should it be his lot to have an encounter with the slayers. So he set an even stricter watch on the hill. And when he saw the ship driving speedily before the pure, cold wind of

73

March towards their shores, he put on his battle clothing, and took his weapons in his hands, and descended the hill, and stood waiting at its foot.

And when Brian and his brothers appeared before him, Midkena cried loudly, "O Sons of Tuireann, welcome and thrice welcome is your coming, slayers and murderers as ye are. For the death of Kian, my pupil and friend, is known to me, and if I die in the attempt I will have vengeance, and be sure ye shall never leave this place alive."

Then Brian bade his brothers stand aside, and he took his long, heavy, gold-hilted sword from out its scabbard, and sprang forward, and so the two heroes attacked each other in a furious and splendid onset. Long they swayed to and fro, but neither would yield although each had received many sore wounds. But at last, just as Midkena's three sons, hearing the crash of steel on steel, came running to their father's aid, Midkena stumbled, and fell to the ground, smitten through the helm by Brian's sharp-edged sword. And when his sons stooped to raise him they saw that he was dead.

And now began a fierce and terrible fight, with the three sons of Midkena on one side, and the three Sons of Tuireann on the other. And had they known of it, men would have been glad to witness such a combat between these great and valiant champions, all skilled in the use of weapons, and speedy and strong in their movements.

The fight raged on without either side yielding ground until the three Sons of Tuireann were bleeding from a hundred dreadful wounds, and the ground beneath them was slippery from the trampling of their feet and the blood they had shed.

Then Brian gathered his remaining strength, and cried out to his brothers—calling on them to make one last effort. And when they heard his voice they lifted their weary heads, and sprang furiously at their foes; and before this mighty onslaught the sons of Midkena fell back, step by step, until at last the Sons of Tuireann lifted their spears, and drove them through the hearts of Midkena's sons—and so the battle ended.

But now that the fight had been fought and won, and the fury of the warriors ebbed away, the Sons of Tuireann began to feel the first weakness from their deep and bloody wounds. Together, and without speech, they turned aside, and threw themselves down on the cool, green softness of grass—and a stupor of deathlike weariness fell upon them, so that they lay motionless as if already dead.

At last Brian raised his head, and spoke his brothers' names, for he did not know if they still lived or not. And when he heard them answer in uncertain and wavering tones, he said, "My dear brothers, now must we rise, and give the three shouts on Midkena's Hill while yet there is breath left to us, for I feel death coming swiftly upon me."

Then Iuchar and Iucharba tried to rise to their feet, but so weak were they from loss of blood that each time they sank back to the ground. And Brian, seeing that they were unable to help themselves, made a last, mighty effort; and drawing himself up with pain and difficulty, he put down a hand to each of them, and lifted them with the strength remaining to him.

And so, with blood flowing freely they stood, each having a foot on the Hill of Midkena, and raised three feeble shouts. Thus did they fulfil the last part of the eric-fine which they had undertaken to pay.

12. The Death of the Sons of Tuireann

WHEN THE last part of their quest was fulfilled, the three Sons of Tuireann felt a great longing to see their own native land again, and their father's house.

So while yet a little strength remained to them, they helped each other's faltering steps, and with much pain and weariness tottered down to the shore, and entering their ship, set sail for the West. And the Fates relented in that hour, and a strong, pure swift wind came out of the north-east, and drove the ship steadily onwards, until there came a day when Brian, who had been gazing towards the western horizon cried, "I can see the mountains of Erin rising out of the sea."

And it was not long after this that he cried again, "Look you, I see Ben Edair now, clear and blue above the waters; and Dun Tuireann shows itself like a small black bird against the sky."

And Iuchar answered, "O my brother, come to us and lift up our heads that we may see green Erin's coasts, for I feel that one glimpse of our own native land would restore our strength. But if we must die, let it be under our father's roof."

Then Brian said, "My beloved brothers, gladly would I come to you but that I fear to move from here. For my wounds have not ceased to bleed, and my strength is ebbing fast."

Then Iuchar replied, "Happily would we give our lives if you might live, for you are the noblest and most valiant champion of Erin, and the pride of our race."

And Brian said, "Could we but hold in our hands the golden apples of Hisberna we could hope to come safely to Erin's shores, and spend our lives in peace henceforward."

But Iuchar answered pitifully, "Enough were it for me to look once more on Erin's hills and our father's house, then strength would flow back into my body as the waters of a river flow into the sea."

So Brian raised himself in his place, and dragging himself painfully to where his brothers lay side by side on the deck, he lifted their heads, and rested them against his breast, and so they remained, while the ship moved slowly nearer and nearer to the longed-for isle.

At last they reached the small harbour on the north side of Ben Edair, and after a long struggle to overcome their growing weakness, they came to land, and supporting each other, they struggled step by anguished step up the sloping path from the shore, until they reached the smooth, soft green plain in front of the house of Tuireann.

Then Brian stood, upheld by his brothers' arms, and cried out, "My father, my father, come out to us your sons, for we can come no further." And their father heard Brian's appeal, and came running out with haste, calling, "My sons, my dear sons, ye have come home."

Then Brian said to his father, "O my father, we are wounded unto death. I beg you to take the cooking-spit and travel with the speed of an arrow to Tara, and give it to the Ildana Lugh, and tell him we have given the three shouts on Midkena's Hill. Now have we paid the eric-fine in full, so plead with him to give you the apples of Hisberna to heal our wounds, or we must die."

Then Tuireann took the spit, and set forth, and he travelled on the pure, soft green wind until he came to Tara, and there he found Lugh the Long-Handed, and gave him the spit and repeated his son's words. But Lugh turned away, and refused to grant the request.

So Tuireann hastened back to his sons with sorrow and foreboding in his heart, being certain that nothing could avail to save them from the doom that was on them.

But when he had told them what Lugh had said, Brian asked his father to take him to Tara, thinking that if Lugh could see his wounds, he would have pity and relent. And so they did.

But when Brian besought Lugh for even one of the apples, Lugh replied, "If you had here all the gold in the earth and offered it to me I would not give it to you—for evil was the deed ye committed when ye slew my father, and no pity did you show him in his hour of need. Therefore never will I forgive you, and only your death can satisfy my vengeance."

And he said,

"For the blood that you spilled,
For the hero you killed,
The deed is avenged, and your doom fulfilled."

Then Brian and his father returned to Tara, and Brian went to where his brothers were awaiting him, and lying down between them, sighed once, and died. And in the same moment his brothers died also.

And when they were dead, their father Tuireann and Ethnea his daughter sang a proud lament, standing hand in hand beside the lifeless corpses; and when their lay was ended, they fell forward on the bodies of the three valiant heroes, and died. And they found burial in one grave.

So ends the story of the Children of Tuireann.

F

THE FATE OF THE
CHILDREN OF LIR

1. The Choosing of the High-King of Erin

LONG AGO, so long that only the oldest chronicles keep a record of it, there was a great battle at Taillten in Erin, between the Tuatha De Danann and the Milesians. And when the battle was over, the De Dananns met together in council, and they decided among themselves to choose a king to reign over the whole nation, so that they might not be any more divided in their loyalties by owing allegiance to sundry princes and lords.

Now there were four noble chiefs above all others to whom this honour might fall, and they were, Bove Derg the son of Dagda; his brother Angus of Brugh on the Boyne, the most skilled man in magic arts in the whole of Erin, known as the chief fairy of the Boyne; Lir of Shee Finnaha, a mighty warrior; and Midir the Haughty, of Bri-Leth. Of these four, only Angus of the Boyne had no desire to be made king, being satisfied to keep to his skills and his learning.

On the chosen day then, all the Tuatha De Danann met together, and after many long hours they decided to elect Bove Derg the son of Dagda as king over the whole De Danann race. And presently, according to custom, they announced their decision publicly—and the four chief nobles who had competed for the choice were waiting to know on which one of them this great honour should fall.

When they heard that Bove Derg was to be king, only one among them was grievously disappointed, and that one was Lir of Shee Finnaha. And so deeply was he offended that he left the place of assembly without a word of farewell to any among them—and without showing his loyalty and acceptance of the newly elected king.

Now the manner of Lir's departure roused all the nobles and chieftains to a fierceness of anger, and they shouted out in council that they would follow after Lir with the speed of a black wind, and slay him with the biting edge of sharp steel, and destroy his house with fire. For they were resolved to punish him because he would not give his fealty to the king they had lawfully chosen.

But when Bove Derg heard what they wished to do, he stood up among them, and said, "Now you have taken me for your king, and so it is my right to give you my commands. And thus it is that I forbid you to follow after Lir—for he is a strong warrior, and has many splendid, invincible men in his territories, and these will rise up to support him should any attempts be made to attack him—and so many will be slain. Let you pay heed to my wishes in this matter."

So the chiefs of the De Dananns obeyed the

commands of Bove Derg, and Lir remained on his own lands, and a great length of days passed. And then a terrible sorrow came upon Lir, for his wife fell ill, and after three days she died—and the silence of mourning brooded like an impenetrable mist over Lir's house, and in his desolate heart.

When these heavy tidings were brought to Bove Derg he thought over them for a while, and then he said to the nobles and warriors assembled at his house, "It has come to my hearing that the wife of Lir of Shee Finnaha is dead, and it seems to me that now I can be of service to him, and he might be willing to accept my friendship. It is known to you all that in my house I have the three most beautiful and variously skilled fair maidens in the whole of Erin, namely my foster children, Alva, Eve and Eva—and it is my thought that one of these maidens might be pleasing to Lir to fill the empty place by his side."

Then all the De Dananns gave their assent to this proposal; and soon messengers were called, and were mounted on swift horses, and sent to Lir; and this is the message they brought him: "Bove Derg, son of Dagda, high-king of Erin, sends you his greetings, and sorrows with you for the death of your wife. And he would have you know that if you will give him your obedience he is willing to give you one of his three beautiful foster-daughters to wife. And you may be sure of his lasting friendship."

When Lir received this message, his heart was

softened, and he repented having given cause of offence to Bove Derg. And on the next day he ordered fifty chariots and horsemen to be brought to his door—and so he set out for Lough Derg, and did not rest nor turn aside until he reached the palace of the king. And when Lir's company were seen approaching, Bove Derg and all his household came out to meet them—and great was the rejoicing among all the people, and in the heart of the king, for Lir was much beloved throughout green Erin.

So Bove Derg took Lir into his palace, and gave him a gentle welcome, and made a great feast for him and his followers. And they were offered soft beds and restful sleep under the king's roof, and there was understanding and amity between them.

Now on the next day, the three foster-daughters of Bove Derg were brought into the great hall by the queen, and sat with her on a high, splendidly carved couch. And these maidens were most lovely to behold, for they were all three as white and golden as lilies—white and delicate their skin, and golden and shining the long, flowing tresses of their hair. And their eyes were blue as the reflection of the sky in the waters of the lough—and their lips were scarlet as rowan berries. And each wore a robe of white linen, cunningly embroidered with threads of gold—and over their shoulders were cloaks of deep, rich green, fastened with golden brooches—and they wore rings of gold on their arms.

Then Bove Derg said to Lir, "Here are my three foster-children—and it is my wish that you choose one among them to be your wife."

And Lir looked at the maidens, and he was filled with astonishment when he saw their beauty, and he said to the king, "Never have I seen any maidens as lovely as these your daughters, and indeed they are all equally fair. So I will choose the eldest among them, for I am sure she will be the noblest of these three."

Then Bove Derg smiled, and he said to Lir, "My daughters are named Eva, and Eve, and Alva —and Eve is the eldest, and she shall be given to you according to your choice." And so it was.

And immediately a splendid wedding feast was made ready in the great hall of the palace, and Lir and Eve were wedded that day to the great joy of Bove Derg and all the De Dananns.

And Lir remained in the palace of the king for two weeks, and after that he summoned his people together and departed for Shee Finnaha, taking his wife with him to his own lands. And when he reached his house, he sent messengers throughout his territory and called all his people together, and held a great and royal feast in honour of his wedding. And so Lir was reconciled to Bove Derg, high-king of Erin.

2. The Children of Lir

WHEN SOME years had passed, Lir's wife Eve bore him two children, and these were of one birth, a boy and a girl named Aedh and Finola; and they were strong, fair-seeming children.

And once again she bore him twin babes, two fine, sturdy sons named Conn and Fiachra; but alas, she died in giving them birth—and Lir was plunged into a sea of sorrow. Indeed, so terrible was his grief that he might have died had it not been for his four lovely babes—but so dear were they to his heart that his mind turned to them for healing, and so his sorrow was lessened.

Now when the news of Eve's death was brought to Bove Derg he was sorely distressed, and so were all his household—and the cries of lamentation rose up into the heavens and were heard far across the plains and hills of Erin. But when the time of mourning had been fulfilled, Bove Derg gathered all his household about him, and also his chief nobles and warriors, and said to them, "Grievous has been the death of our dear foster-child, not only for our own sakes, but also because of her husband Lir, whose friendship and loyalty are very precious to us. Yet there is no need for this happy alliance to end—for rather than that it should be broken I will give him my second foster-daughter Eva to be his wife."

So messengers travelled with the speed of the green wind of March to Lir's house in Shee Finnaha and told him of Bove Derg's words—and his heart was comforted, and he agreed to the king's proposal. And in no long time after this he came to the palace of the high-king, and was married to the maiden Eva with her goodwill; and soon afterwards he brought her to his home.

Now when Eva saw the four Children of Lir, her heart was filled with delight and tenderness; and so her greatest joy was in the nursing and care of the babes, and each day her love for them was deepened. And Lir too found his happiness in his little ones, and he ordained that they were to be put to sleep near his own couch, so that at the hour when the night meets the day he might rise and go to them, to talk with them and caress them.

And as the children grew older, Bove Derg too came to know and love them almost as dearly as their father Lir; for it was his custom to come to Shee Finnaha several times each year to see them; and sometimes they went with him to his palace, and there he kept them as long as he might, and grieved to let them go home again.

Also, at this time the De Dananns had chosen to celebrate the Feast of Age at the houses of their chief nobles in turn; for this feast had been begun by Mannanan Mac Lir, and all who were present were saved ever after from sickness, loss of strength or old age. And whenever this festival came to be held at Shee Finnaha, the four Children of Lir were a source of great wonder and delight to all the assembly. And so gentle and sweet-natured were the four, that no one who saw them could help loving them with all their hearts.

Now, as the children grew into their youthful manhood and womanhood, and loveliness lay upon them as the colour lies on the petals of a flower, their stepmother was seized by a venomous jealousy; for she imagined that Lir her husband and all who saw the children were neglectful of her, and so her love was turned to hatred.

So bitter was her jealousy that an illness came upon her, and for the space of a whole year she lay in her bed, filled with black and evil thoughts, and plotting to be rid of the four Children of Lir. And at last she conceived an idea which she hastened to carry out.

On a certain day, then, she called for her horses to be yoked to her chariot, and she told the children that she was going speedily to the palace of Bove Derg, and wished them to accompany her. Now Finola shrank in horror when her stepmother spoke, for she had had a dark and terrifying dream, in which it was revealed to her that Eva desired the death of her and her brothers: but she could not escape, nor refuse her stepmother's commands.

So they set forth in the golden light of early morning, with the delicate blue skies of spring over their heads, and a chiming melody of bird-song in their ears, and the scent of innumerable flowers blown around them by the green wind of March.

And when they had gone a little way upon the road, Eva turned to her attendants, and ordered them to slay the children instantly.

"If ye will do this, be sure ye shall be richly rewarded," she said, "for I can no longer endure to be neglected and spurned by all on account of these wretches."

But the men heard her words with horror, and replied, "Foul and cruel is this deed you would have us do, O Eva; surely great evil will fall upon you for such a thought."

But so determined was she to be rid of them, that she snatched up a sword, and would have slain them herself had not the weakness of her woman's arm prevented her. So they set forth once more, and did not halt on the way until they came to Lough Darvra, and there they all alighted on the ground, and unyoked the horses by the shore of the lake.

Then Eva led the children to the water's edge—and suddenly smiled gently, and bade them bathe and refresh themselves. But when the children were swimming in the clear, cool waters, she took a wand of sorcery and magic from under her cloak, and reached out, and touched them one by one; and lo, they were turned into four beautiful swans, with feathers soft and white as snow. And so she stood, and spoke to them thus:

"Noisy are the waters of the sea in a storm,
Harsh are the voices of the clamorous birds
  round the rocks,
Away, away ye swans to your home on the
  breast of the waters.
Very cold will be your sleep through the long,
  chill nights,
Hard is your lot, nor shall your friends save
  you this day,
For I have spoken aloud the words of doom."

Then the four Children of Lir turned their eyes towards their stepmother, and Finola spoke, and she said, "Treacherous and terrible is the deed you have done this day, O Eva; for we trusted in your friendship and love, and you have betrayed us without a cause. But the deed will be avenged, and a worse doom shall overtake you than ours."

Then she spoke again, and said to her stepmother, "Tell us now how long we must remain in this shape, for it is better that we may know how to endure our misery."

And Eva answered, "It were better that ye had not asked me this question, but I will not conceal the truth from you. Three hundred long years you must dwell on the smooth, clear waters of Darvra; and again another three hundred on the turbulent

Sea of Moyle, between Erin and Alba's shores; yet again, three hundred at Irros Domnann, and at Innis Glora on the Western Sea. So you shall remain until Largnen, prince of the north, weds with Decca, the princess of the southern lands. Aye, even until the Taillkenn Patrick shall come to Erin, and ye hear the silver-ringing voice of the Christian bell. And neither by my power, nor yet the power of those who love you shall ye be freed at the last."

Then as she spoke her heart was somewhat softened, and she began to repent of her wicked deed, and she said, "I cannot restore you again to your own shapes—but you may keep your own human speech, and your human reason. And ye shall have the power to sing such fairy sweet sad music that it shall excel all the music in the world, and all who hear it shall be lulled to rest."

Then she bade them farewell, and having ordered her horses to be yoked again to the chariot she departed westwards; and the four white, beautiful swans were left lonely on the surface of the lake, with the knowledge of their dreadful doom singing its sad lament in their hearts.

3. The First
Three Hundred Years

Now when Eva had left the shores of the lake, she ordered the horses to be turned towards Lough Derg—and soon enough she came to the palace of the high-king, and received a gentle and friendly greeting from all the chieftains and the king her foster father. And after a little while Bove Derg asked Eva why the Children of Lir were not with her, for she knew how well he loved to have them under his roof.

Then Eva said, "Sorry am I to tell you that a great cloud of mistrust has filled the mind of Lir, and he refused to let the children come with me, saying that he no longer felt friendly towards you. I do not know why this should be, O my father, and I am grieved to have to bring such tidings."

The king was deeply disturbed by these words, and exclaimed, "How can it be thus, for I have given no cause of offence to Lir? And the children I have come to love as if they were indeed my own."

Now when Bove Derg was alone, he thought much on this matter—and the more he thought, the less could he understand it—and at last he began to fear some treachery on the part of Eva. So he called for some trustworthy and swift messengers, and sent them with the speed of hawks to the north, to seek out Lir, and find the truth in the story.

When Lir heard what the messengers had to say he was greatly astonished, and he asked quickly if the children had followed after Eva to the palace. They answered, "Nay, for the Lady Eva told Bove Derg that you had ordered them to stay by your side."

Then Lir was filled with terror, for he had a dreadful foreboding that Eva had slain his four lovely children. And so, next day, when the first spear of light in the east drove the darkness before it, he mounted his chariot, and set out for the king's palace, and travelled on the strong, pure cold north wind until he arrived at the shores of Lough Darvra.

Now the four swans were resting on the waters of the lake where they were doomed to remain for three hundred long years, and they saw the company coming towards them; and Finola said to her brothers, "See the bright gleam of many spears, and the glitter of armour and shields. Well do I know that proud, invincible band of warriors, the hosts of royal Lir our father. Come, my brothers, let us give him welcome, and mourn with him on this sorrowful day."

Then the four birds stretched their long graceful necks, and opened their mighty wings, and lifted

G

themselves on to the currents of the air, which sang with the music of their flight, and alighted on the surface of the waters edging the lake.

When Lir and his followers reached the shore he saw the swans, and heard them speaking in human voices; and being filled with amazement he hastened to ask the birds how this had come to pass, for he was sure that they lay under some enchantment.

Then Finola spoke, and she said, "O Lir, our dear father, let you know that we are your four children, and through the malice and witchcraft of our stepmother we are changed into swans, and none may help us."

When Lir and his people heard these words they were overcome with grief, and filled the air with loud and terrible cries, so that all the birds on the lake and around that place stretched their wings and took flight, nor stayed their course until they had gone far into the south lands of Erin.

And after a time, Lir said to the swans, "Can no one restore you to your rightful shapes? Sure it is that Angus of the Brugh is the most skilled man of magical arts in the world; I will go to him and ask him to relieve you from this evil spell."

But Finola replied, "O my father, not even Angus of the Brugh can aid us—for we must keep these shapes until Largnen from the north and Decca from the south are wed. Three hundred years must we stay on these waters, and again on the sea-waters of Moyle; and yet another three hundred on the Sea of Glora to the west. For we may not escape from our doom until the Taillkenn brings the lamp of his pure faith into Erin, and we can hear the silver chiming of the Christian bell."

Then Lir and his people raised yet more cries of grief and lamentation. And Lir said, "Surely ye can leave these cold, grey waters, and come to land, and return with me to your home and dwell there. For you still have the gift of human speech, and so we can all converse together, and this will ease our sorrow." But Finola answered, "We may not leave the waters of the lake, for that is part of the doom laid upon us. But remain with us this night, and we will sing our songs in your ears, and ye shall forget your grief and enjoy a sweet rest and sleep."

So Lir and his people waited by the shores of the lake; and the swans raised their voices, and instantly the air was filled with a charm of soft, sad fairy music, very clear and sweet, and repeated over and over like a lullaby. And Lir and his followers sank into a deep, calm sleep—and night covered them with a cloak of peace.

At dawn the next morning Lir rose up, resolved to seek out Eva and destroy her. And before he went, he bade farewell to his children, and this is what he said:

"O Shee Finnaha, green land of a loved
    dwelling;
Gloomy is the life of those without a house;

Sad is the beat and plaint of waves upon the
   shore,
O dark Aedh, and bright Fiachra, gentle boy—
O small Conn of the golden hair, and prideful
   lovely Finola,
Dreadful is the savage strife of the fierce
   waves in the winter's days,
And to pass my years without children in the
   house is a great sorrow.
My dear children are lost to me in a wild
   waste of waters,
Today am I aged and old, for a cruel doom
   has spoken.
Farewell, my little children, be sure I shall
   watch over you.
The good household lies empty. Farewell."

Now when Lir reached the palace of Bove Derg,
he found Eva with the king—and before he could
speak, Bove Derg began to reproach him because
the children were not with him, and bitter were
the words of the king. But Lir was not angered,
knowing as he did the truth of the matter, and he
said to Bove Derg, "Alas, it is not myself, O king,
who prevented the coming of the children. It is
Eva, your own foster-child, who has done a wicked
and cruel deed—for in her relentless jealousy she
has changed my four lovely children into four
white swans on Darvra's lake."

Then Bove Derg turned, and looked at Eva, and
by the change in her countenance he knew that Lir

spoke the truth—and he was filled with a fiery anger and dismay—and he said to Eva, "Now I swear that it shall be worse for thee than for the Children of Lir, for their suffering shall cease, but you shall have such punishment as knows no easing." And many more fierce and bitter words he spoke to her. And at last he asked her what shape of all others she most feared and abhorred, whether it were in the air, on the earth, or below it. And after a long silence she answered slowly, "A demon of the air."

"Then take that form for ever," said Bove Derg; and so speaking, he struck her with a magic, druidical wand. And in the instant, before their horrified eyes, she changed into a demon of the air—and great black, scaly wings sprang from her shoulders, and her nails lengthened into curving, sharp talons, and her eyes shone with baffled hate and fury. So she stood for a moment, and then, uttering a shrill scream of despair, she opened her wings, and flew out of the doorway and up into the clouds—and for all that is known, she flies there to this day.

And this was the fate of the children's stepmother.

4. The Sea
of Moyle

NOW SOON after this, Bove Derg and the De Danann people assembled together on the shores of Lough Darvra, for the news had spread over all Erin, and all men were amazed and grieved at the fate of the beautiful Children of Lir; moreover, they had heard of the wonderful fairy music of the swans' voices, and wished to hear it for themselves. For it is said in the annals of Erin that no music in the world has ever been compared to the singing of the swans.

In this manner time passed swiftly enough—for by day the swans conversed with the men of Erin and with their father Lir and all their childhood's friends. And by night they sang their rich strange fairy songs—and all who heard them forgot grief, and pain, weariness and age, and any suffering whatsoever, and slept a sweet and quiet sleep, waking always to happiness and a lasting brightness around them. And so they continued for a full three hundred years.

Then at last one day Finola said to her brothers, "Did you know, my dear brothers, that the time has come for us to leave these quiet waters, for we may spend only one more night in this place?"

Sad was that day for the four swans, and for all their friends and kinsfolk. For here the time had fled without change or stress to mar the golden hours—day drifting peacefully into the arms of night, and night in turn yielding her place to the springing clear light of dawn. But now all this was at an end, and the swans must live on the dark and stormy Sea of Moyle, solitary and divided from all human companions.

When the De Danann people heard that the swans must leave them so soon they were overcome with grief, and their cries of lamentation echoed from shore to shore of the lake and were thrown back to them in echoes from the far hills.

Very early, then, on the next morning, the swans came to the margin of the lake, and said farewell to their father Lir, and to all whom they knew and loved; and Finola sang a small sad song to the silent people:

"Dear to us are these cool reed-enclosed
        waters—
Darvra has been a home to us; farewell, O Lir
        our father,
Farewell to our friends and kinsfolk,
Pleasant has been a loving sojourn amongst you.
Now our doom calls; fearful is the future
        before us
For we must live through long ages on cruel
        Moyle

In dread and loneliness.
Arise now my brothers for we must go
Leaving a measureless grief behind us—
   Farewell."

Then the four beautiful, proud swans spread
their strong wings, and rose high into the air—and
the sound of their flight was as the strings of many
harps when plucked by a master hand. For a while
they hovered over the lake, then with necks outstretched they flew northwards, and passed over
the tracks of the air until they reached the Sea of
Moyle between the shores of Erin and Alba—and
there they alighted, and prepared themselves to
endure patiently until time should release them
from their bondage.

And so bitter was the grief of the men of Erin
at their departure that they made a new law on that
day, and proclaimed it throughout the length and

breadth of the land—and it was that no man might kill a swan in Erin's lands while the world endured —and thus it is to this day.

Now hard was the plight of the Children of Lir, and miserable their dwelling-place on tempestuous Moyle. For the harsh, black rocky coasts stretched far on all sides, and around them surged the wild dark waters, and they were filled with dread and despair. So they lived, suffering much from cold, hunger and loneliness until one night a fierce tempest swept down upon the waters—and a strange wailing wind circled in the air above them.

Then Finola said to her brothers, "Ill prepared are we to meet the terrors of this night, for it is certain that this great storm will tear us apart one from the other in the darkness. Let us appoint a place of meeting lest we wander to and fro seeking each other in vain."

And they answered her, "Dear sister, wisdom is in your speech—let us agree to meet at Carrick-narone on that great rock known to all of us."

Soon midnight came, and with it the storm rose to its height—a roaring angry wind swept over the billows of the sea, sharp lightnings darted from the skies, and the thunder of the waters out-rivalled the thunder of the flying clouds overhead.

The swans were separated in the darkness, and scattered in different directions; and so all night long they were tossed hither and thither, battered and helpless, their very lives endangered by the fury of the elements.

At last, as the grey, dull morning light broke over the heaving waters, the storm lessened—and after a time the sea became calm again, and the winds dropped suddenly to rest. Then Finola smoothed down her ruffled and torn feathers, and swam eagerly to Carricknarone—but none of her brothers were there to greet her—nor could she see them as she searched the wide face of the waters from the summit of the rock.

Now Finola was filled with terror lest her brothers were lost in the storm, and she feared she would never see them again. But as she lifted her voice in a plaintive chant, she saw Conn coming slowly across the waves towards her, his head drooping, and his feathers encrusted with the salty spray—and joyful was her welcome.

It was not long after this, while they talked together of the dreadful night that Fiachra appeared in the distance—so feebly did he move that they feared he might not reach the rock—but at last he struggled out of the water, and stood beside them, so spent with cold and hardship that he could not speak.

Then Finola said to them, "Now my dear brothers, take shelter under the feathers of my wings, which will give you warmth and comfort. If only Aedh were here now our happiness would be complete."

So the two brothers placed themselves under Finola's wings, and found rest and security there.

Suddenly they saw Aedh coming fast to join

them, his neck outstretched, and his plumage smoothly shining and dry—and gladly did they welcome him. Thus they outlived that storm, and were reunited in safety.

5. The Fairy Host

So time passed, and there came a January night when wind and frost held the earth and sea in an iron grip, so that the waters turned to blocks of ice.

The four swans had remained at Carricknarone, and when morning came they ventured to stir from the icy surface—but their feet and wings were held fast; and when, after long striving, they freed themselves, they left feathers and skin from their feet still fast in the ice.

At last they forced themselves to enter the swift stream of Moyle, and swim nearer to the coast. The cruel salty water entered their wounds, and fearful was the pain they endured; for they were forbidden by their doom to leave the sea waters of Moyle. But many long, weary weeks went by before their wounds were healed, and the feathers on their wings and breasts grew again. So they lived for a great number of years, flying from shore to shore, and sometimes visiting Alba's rocky coasts —but always they returned to the sea-stream of Moyle.

On a certain day they flew to the mouth of the River Bann, which lay to the north—and while they rested and preened their feathers, they saw a proud-seeming company of horsemen coming towards them out of the south-west. They wore garments of many brilliant colours, reds, blues, greens, saffron—and their weapons glittered like silver in the sunshine. They rode on white, splendid horses, and snatches of song could be heard as if the host were light of heart, and merry on this golden day.

Then Finola said to her brothers, "Is this company familiar to your eyes?"

And they answered, "No sister, but perhaps it is a troop of our people moving from one chieftain's lands to another."

When the company was near enough to see the swans, they turned at once and rode towards them, and soon were within speaking distance. And in a little time it was made known that these were De Dananns, a part of the Fairy Host, under the leadership of Aedh the Keenwitted, and Fergus the Chess-player, and these two were the sons of Bove Derg, high-king of Erin. They had been sent forth to find the Children of Lir, and long and hard had they sought them up and down the coasts of Erin—and great was the rejoicing now that the search was ended.

The Children of Lir asked anxiously how it fared with their father, and all their kinsfolk and friends —and Fergus answered, "Ye may rest content, for they are well—and at this time Bove Derg our father and the greater part of the De Danann people are gathered together at the house of your father Lir at Shee Finnaha, to celebrate the Feast of Age, and there is much feasting and merriment. But their happiness cannot be complete until we bring them tidings of how it has been with you since you left Lough Darvra, for sorely are you missed by all."

"Bitter has been our sojourn on the cold cruel waters of Moyle," said Finola—and speaking in turns, she and her brothers told Fergus and Aedh and the Fairy Host of all the suffering and misery they had endured. But glad were they to see their own people, for their loneliness was eased, and they sent many loving messages to their father and to all their friends.

Soon after this they took a sorrowful farewell of the Fairy Host, and flew back to Moyle, and the company returned to Shee Finnaha, and related all that they had been told by the swans. Then the chiefs were grieved beyond measure, and deep was their longing to help the Children of Lir —but there was nothing they might do until the enchantment was ended and the swans were free to return to their own shapes once more.

But one day the wheel of time brought the second three hundred years to an end, and Finola and her brothers gladly turned away from the Sea of Moyle, and took their flight to the West, until they reached Irros Domnann, and alighted on the sea which surges around the isle of Glora.

Now after they had been there for a while, it chanced that a young man named Ebric, of a chieftain's house, to whom the lands running down to the shore belonged, walked one day beside the water's edge. And soon his eyes were drawn to the swans, resting motionless on the surface of the gently moving waves, and he wondered much how they came to be there. And the same evening, standing on the cliff-top to watch a strange vessel with brightly coloured sails driven fast before the breeze, he heard the songs of the swans, borne to him on the wind. So great was his delight in the sad, sweet music, that very early next morning he went down to the shore, and there he saw the swans, and to his astonishment heard them speaking to each other in human speech.

At last he ventured near to them, and they gave him a gentle and courteous greeting—and a great love sprang up between Ebric and the Children of Lir, for he sustained them in their loneliness, and visited them daily. And it was he who preserved their story so that it can be related to this day—for he told all his friends and neighbours of the singing swans, and the tale was handed down from father to son for many hundreds of years—until it came to be written down by bards and poets and preserved for us.

But although the swans had Ebric to comfort them, they still suffered cruel hardships; and there came a dark winter's night when the frost was so terrible that the whole surface of the sea from that place to Achill was frozen with a glistening sheet of ice; and after the frost came a drifting cloud of snow, driven furiously onward by a howling northerly wind.

It was then that the three sons of Lir felt that they could no longer endure such fearful suffering, and they cried aloud in piteous voices, calling to their sister to comfort them; and so for a time all four swans wept and lamented together, and the hours of the night seemed endless.

But when the cold grey light of dawn broke over the stark and frozen earth, Finola said, "My dear brothers—we have heard of the great and splendid God Who made the world, and Whose hand can deliver us. Let us trust that He may send us some help that we may bear this enchantment to the end."

And her brothers praised her for her wisdom, and together they all cried upon the Lord of Heaven for His protection and aid. And He heard their plaint, and from that time onwards, neither cold, nor heat, nor tempest had any power to hurt them while they remained on the Western Sea.

6. The Christian Bell

AT LAST the time came when Finola said again to her brothers, "Now we may lift our wings and depart from this place, for we have endured to the end of our appointed years. Let us fly speedily back to Shee Finnaha and visit our dear father and kinsfolk."

Glad were her brothers Conn, Aedh and Fiachra to hear these words, and joyfully they stretched their strong pinions, and lifted themselves on to the currents of the air, and let the pure, soft blue wind of the west bear them to their home lands. Soon enough they saw the familiar hills and plains beneath them, and swiftly they sank earthwards and alighted near their father's dwelling at Shee Finnaha.

But when they came to the ground, they saw that their father's halls were desolate and deserted, the walls crumbling and overgrown by nettles and long twining grasses; nor was there any other sign of human habitation, or sound of human voice.

Then the Children of Lir drew close together and uttered loud, mournful cries, and beat their wings together in their grief and despair. And Finola sang this lay:

"Gone are the proud companies of warriors,
Our father and kinsfolk have departed—
Sad, sad is our return, for evil is our plight,
Desolate this day is Shee Finnaha,
Desolate are the four Children of Lir,
The happy household lives no more, nor Lir
    our father.
Sad is the cry of the heron over the empty
    dwellings,
Grief is in the voice of the curlew,
Sorrowful is the music made by the wind
    amidst the ruins of our father's house.
Now must we remain for ever homeless and
    desolate—
Alas for the Children of Lir."

Throughout the long night the swans remained in the ruins of the palace, lamenting to the heavens, and weeping in the place where they had been born. And when morning came, they took wing, and fled through the air until they came to Inis Glora, and they alighted there on a small, smooth lake, and rested for a while, overcome by their bitter loss.

But after a time they began to sing their sweet sad fairy songs again, and these songs were carried on the wind over water and land, so that all the birds of the district heard them, and came in great flocks, and settled on the lake, and on its shores, attracted by the voices of the swans. And so that place came to be known as the Lake of the Birds.

So the Children of Lir passed their lonely days, flying hither and thither in search of food, but never finding any of their own people in their travels. Sometimes they went to Iniskea, the Isle of the Crane; for here lived the solitary bird which had been there since the world began, and they held converse with it. Again they would visit distant Achill, or fly far southwards to the sea-rocks of Dhuinn, and to all the islands of the Western Sea.

Thus they lived from year to year, until at last the holy Taillkenn Patrick came to Erin, bringing with him the pure Christian faith; and soon after this, the blessed hermit Kemoc came to dwell on Inis Glora, and live his solitary life there amid the surging, restless seas.

Now on the night of his coming, the hermit

struck his bell, and the loud notes rang out at the time of matins. When the Children of Lir heard the sound carried to them on the night wind they trembled with fear, and flew to and fro in the darkness, made restless by terror. But after a while Finola said to her brothers, "It seems to me that this is a sound for which we have long been waiting."

And her brothers answered, "What think you it means, dear sister—for to us it is a strange and fearful voice?"

"I think it may well be the sound of that Christian bell which is a token that we shall soon be freed of this evil enchantment—so let us rejoice, my brothers, and praise God."

Then her brothers took courage from her words, and they raised their voices and sang a low, sweet fairy song of thanksgiving to the King of Heaven.

Now Kemoc had been sent to Inis Glora to seek out the Children of Lir. So when he heard the beautiful, soft music of the swans' voices he knew that his search was ended; and when the morning light struck down in a long, golden shaft across the water, he ran to the shore, and saw the swans resting on the sea, with their proud heads bent in peaceful converse, and he called out to them to say if they were indeed the Children of Lir.

When he heard their answer he rejoiced, and said to them, "It is to seek you four that I am come to this island out of all the isles of Erin. And it is in this place that ye shall be freed from your enchantment—so lay aside your fears, and come to land, and I will care for you."

So they trusted him, and flew swiftly to his side, and he brought them to his dwelling, and gave them his comfort and protection. And he sent for a skilled worker in metals, and caused him to make two slender, shining chains of silver—and with one he linked together Aedh and Finola, and with the other he joined Fiachra and Conn.

And so, day by day, he instructed the Children of Lir in the pure Christian faith, and fed and cared for them—and great was the love between the swans and this holy man—and thus at last, after their long years of suffering and hardship they knew happiness again.

7. The Death of the Children of Lir

NOW THE last part of Eva's prophecy had been fulfilled, for some years past Largnen, king of Connacht, had taken to wife Decca, the daughter of Finnin, king of Munster, and so north and south were united.

On a certain day then, a traveller brought word to the queen regarding the singing swans of Inis Glora. And when she questioned him further, he told her the whole sad story of the Children of Lir—but the queen was seized with a strong desire to possess these wonderful birds, and cared little for their former misery.

So she went to Largnen her husband, and related the traveller's tale, and besought him to send swift messengers to the hermit Kemoc, ordering him to send the swans to the king's house; but Largnen refused her request.

When she had pleaded for some time in vain, Decca was filled with anger, and said that whether he would aid her or not, she was determined to have the swans for herself. And she would not sleep that night under the king's roof, but departed from the palace within the hour, and went with the speed of a swallow to her father's house in the southern lands.

When Largnen found that she had left him, he sent messengers after her in all haste, taking his promise that he would try to obtain the swans as soon as might be; but Decca had already reached her father's lands at Killaloe before the messengers overtook her.

Howsoever, when the king's message was made known to her, she took a speedy farewell of her father and kinsfolk, and returned instantly to Connacht—and as soon as she was come into the palace, Largnen sent a courteous request to Kemoc that he should send the birds to the queen; but this the hermit refused to do.

Now Largnen in his turn became very angry, and he called for his chariot and horses, and a goodly troop of warriors, and set out for Inis Glora.

As soon as he arrived at Kemoc's house, he asked the hermit sternly if it was true that he had refused to yield up the swans to Queen Decca, and Kemoc answered boldly that it was so.

When the king heard these words, he was exceedingly wroth, and going into the church where the swans stood, he seized the silver chains in his hands, and dragged the Children of Lir roughly from the altar stone, purposing to take them by force to the queen. And as he departed Kemoc ran after him, greatly distressed lest the swans should suffer a hurt.

The king had only gone a few paces when suddenly the snow-white plumage of the swans melted into the air and was dissolved—and there stood four human forms, those of an old and feeble woman, and three ancient men, wrinkled and bent, with pure white hair.

When Largnen saw this, he was overcome with terror, and releasing the chains instantly fled

from the place without speaking, while Kemoc hurled bitter denunciations after him.

Then, finding themselves once more alone with the hermit, the Children of Lir gathered around him, and Finola said, "O holy Kemoc, the hour of our death draws near—and therefore we ask of you to baptise us without further delay. Sorrowful will be our parting from one another, for great is the love we bear you. Let you make us a grave in this place, and lay us in it together—and so we shall remain close to each other in death as we have been in life."

Then she chanted this lay:

"Hasten, O Kemoc, and shrive us in this hour.
Let us be cleansed in holy baptism,
Before death takes us from you.
Dig our grave soon—a deep grave—
Let Conn be on my right side
Fiachra on my left;
Let Aedh stand before my breast.
Close has been the love that bound us,
So let our arms be twined together—
Now shall we rest for evermore
In the shade of the little church
Where first we heard the sound of the
    Christian bell."

So Kemoc the hermit baptised the Children of Lir, and shrived them of their sins, and when this was done, they smiled sweetly upon him, and closed their eyes in death.

And when Kemoc raised his tear-wet eyes, he saw before him as in a vision four lovely, fair children, with shining, joyful faces, and curving silver wings on their shoulders. And as he looked in amazement, they raised their hands to him in a gesture of farewell, and vanished from his sight. And his heart, which had been heavy with sorrow, was lightened, and he wept for gladness.

So he caused a deep grave to be dug in the shelter of the little church, and he buried the Children of Lir as Finola had requested him, with Conn at her right hand, Fiachra at her left, and Aedh standing before her. And he raised a tombstone, and engraved their names upon it in ogham —and he performed the holy rites of burial, and sang a lament over them.

So ends the sorrowful story of the Children of Lir.

DEIRDRE AND THE
SONS OF UISNE

1. The Foretelling

LONG, LONG ago in the morning of the world, there lived in the island of Erin, now spoken of as Ireland, a man named Colum the Harper. This man was the music-maker to King Conchobor, King of Ulster, and had his place at the court, and was held high in the esteem of all who knew him.

Now on a certain day, his wife came to him and told him that soon they were to have a child; and great was the joy in his heart, for they had been married for many years, but never had the blessing of a child come to them. And so it seemed as if the sunshine had never been so warm and golden, nor the grass so bright and green, or the music of the sea so full of happiness.

But a thing was to happen which cast a black shadow over this richly-coloured hour. For when Colum next sat in the King's hall, surrounded by all the heroes and knights of Ulster, and, impelled by the depth of his own rejoicing, told them the glad tidings, crying upon them to share in his delight, an ancient and renowned Druid arose in his place, and spoke:

"My Lord King, ye noble heroes, and you Colum, singer of proud songs—a darkness fell upon my mind at your words. And now, I see a great sea of blood, a crimson sea, foaming high and terrible to fill our valleys. And I foretell that this child who is to be born will be a sharp sword to sever Ulster's tree, and to strike discord between the hearts of friends and kinsfolk. And because of the child three of Erin's greatest heroes shall meet their death, and many others too shall turn sightless eyes to the heavens."

Then consternation and horror seized all the assembled company, and a rustle as of withered leaves in autumn ran round the hall, for Conchobor and his knights knew well that here was a true word; and many cried out that the child must be slain at birth, and thus the dreadful doom might be averted.

Only Colum sat silent on his stool, his fingers plucking at his harp strings so that they sent out a harsh, jangling sound, and his face ashen in colour as the hearth when the fire had gone dead.

Then the King's voice was heard above the discordant mutterings and dismayed cries of the knights.

"Can you tell us if the child shall be a boy or a girl, old man? Can you see this in the mists of the future?"

And the Druid answered, "I see a girl child, with eyes like stars, a face of ivory and rose, and hair silken and glittering golden as sunlight—such beauty shall be hers as has not been seen in the memory of man."

Once again a clamour broke out in the hall, but

it sank to silence as the King stood up in his place. Tall he was as a fine, straight tree, and his eyes were blue as the sea on a calm day; he wore a scarlet cloak fastened with a golden clasp, and three broad bands of gold on his right arm, and

129

I

his voice was like the wind swelling in a pine wood.

"Shame be it upon us men of Ulster that we should profane the hospitality of our house by talk of such a cruel deed. Now I decree that when the child is born, she must be taken to a far and lonely rath, where none may see her save the birds and beasts, and let her be brought up there by a foster-mother of my choosing, and so kept in seclusion while she lives. And so shall the evil be withheld."

And turning to Colum he asked, "Do you agree to this plan? For it is in my heart that only in this manner can the child be allowed to come to womanhood."

Then Colum in his turn stood up and spoke.

"Grateful am I, O King, for your forbearance, for well might you have commanded the slaying of the babe. And if my wife and I may not have the happiness of bringing up the child as other men may do with their children, yet we shall know that she is alive and cared for, for she is under your hand; and justice I have always had from you."

And so it was settled, and all were satisfied that the direful prophecy would be brought to nought —so that laughter and cheerful voices were heard again round the King's table. Brightly flashed the great cups, studded with green and crimson jewels and filled with mead to the brim, as the knights drank a toast to their King's wisdom. Many were the jests and the light words spoken. Only the ancient Druid sat silent and withdrawn in his chair, and Colum rose and left the hall, walking slowly with a dragging step and his head bowed, as if old age had come upon him within the hour.

On a clear, starlit night soon afterwards the baby was born, and her parents decided to call her Deirdre.

She was the most beautiful baby indeed, as the Druid had foretold. Soft, silken hair covered her little head; her ears were like exquisite shells; she had long, curling eyelashes, and eyes blue as speedwells; her mouth was like a rosebud, and her tiny hands were so perfect that it was a wonder to see them.

But alas for her poor parents, a cruel fate had decreed that they must part with their treasure; only a brief day were they given into which to pour all the love they had for the little one—and on the next night there was a stamping of horses' hooves outside the house, and the King's messenger knocking with a heavy hand upon the door.

"I am come to take the child," he told them, "for none may see her, or know of her destination. But here with me is the good foster-mother chosen by the King, and the babe will be safe in her keeping."

Then with tears and bitter grief they gave the little one into the man's arms, and soon the sound of hoof-beats died away in the stillness, and it was as if a lovely dream had been born and faded

within the hour for Colum the Harper and his wife.

So Deirdre was carried away in the mysterious starlight to a lonely hill fort, in a far and lonely place; so distant and hard of access was the glen leading up to the fort that no one ever went there from one year to another. In this solitary but beautiful place, then, Deirdre spent her childhood days. For soon she grew from an infant to a child, and from a child to a girl, and from a girl into a maiden of a strange and surpassing loveliness.

She had eyes like the blue of the skies; a head of pale, fair hair that shone like silver fire, and so long and fine that she could wrap herself in it; her skin was creamy like ivory, and her feet and hands were white and delicately formed; and her voice was soft, and low and musical, so that beasts and birds came to her call without fear. She could run like a deer, and her laughter rang out in that silent glen like a chime of silver bells.

Deep was the love and pride of the foster-mother in the girl, and she taught her all she knew of knowledge; the names of the birds which came in flocks around the rath in spring—the colours of their feathers, and the calls they made, and the places where they built their nests and laid their softly tinted eggs. Deirdre knew each by its name.

And together they walked on the hill tracks, and over the fields, and as they went Deirdre would give cries of joy at sight of all the tiny flowers, and would carry bunches of them back to the house; and these she learnt to know also.

And as she got older, there were the stars in the night sky. Often, in the warm, summer nights, those two would sit outside the house door, and the nurse would point to first one, and then another, naming the old names that had been on the lips of men since the world began, and the child would repeat them after her, her voice low with wonder and delight.

When she was big enough to go out by herself, the woman plaited a little flat basket for her of the stems of reeds and rushes growing in the stream, and in this she would put a few oaten cakes of her own baking, and a jar of milk, and perhaps a bit of honeycomb. And Deirdre would take this basket, and wander away over the stony paths among the great stretches of heather—or climb down into the fields below, and throw herself down on the sun-warmed grass; and putting her ear to the ground, she would listen to all the sounds not heard by those who never come close enough to the earth. Or she would lie there, looking through the stems of the grasses, and watching a beetle climbing slowly and carefully up a stalk, or a brilliantly coloured butterfly flitting lightly over the up-turned faces of the daisies.

So the long, drowsy day would pass, and when evening fell, she would go back to the rath, and be welcomed with a loving kiss, and there would be the happiness of telling all she had seen and heard and done in the hours of her absence. And the foster-mother would listen, and smile, and ask a question now and again, and presently they would seek their beds, and sink into a dreamless sleep.

And in all this time, never once had Deirdre seen a human soul but her nurse, and the woman Laborcham. Men she had heard about from them both—for they spoke together of the King, and of the knights of the Red Branch and their deeds of valour—but no man had ever come to the rath. And the glen did not seem a lonely place for Deirdre, for she had her foster-mother, and all the beasts and birds were her friends—and never did she long to be in another place. Not at first.

But as she grew older, she sometimes wondered what sort of a house King Conchobor had for his dwelling, and wished she too could see the knights going to and fro in their scarlet and blue and green

cloaks. And much she wondered what sort of country lay beyond the mountains, and what it was like to live near the sea, whose waves she could hear faintly in the distance on a still day. But she felt no surge of discontent, and the time passed pleasantly, and her days were happy.

Now the woman Laborcham was a messenger of King Conchobor's, and twice a year he sent her to see the maiden, and to bring him news of her welfare. And always the woman, on her return from the glen, told Conchobor that never before in the history of the world had such perfect loveliness been seen.

So she reported, and the King rejoiced to think that Deirdre was safely concealed from the eyes of men; for all the knights knew that heavy was the King's hand, and fierce his wrath if provoked, and none dared visit the distant fort. Also, from the beginning, Conchobor was resolved to take Deirdre to wife when she had come to her woman's years; but he was careful to keep his counsel in this matter.

And so time wore away, and smiling spring became golden summer; and summer faded to let the purple and crimson autumn take its place; and then in turn autumn too passed away, yielding place to rains, and wind, and the earth was covered in a soft mantle of snow.

So the years fell, one by one, into the lap of Time, and Deirdre grew, and became ever more beautiful.

2. The Hunter

NOW THE time came when Deirdre reached the age of fourteen years. Slim and straight she was as a young larch tree, and supple as a willow sapling. And her intelligence and goodness of heart were at one with her outward beauty.

Her foster-mother had shown her how to bake the oaten cakes between flat stones on the hearth, and to cook a fine meat broth with fresh picked herbs thrown in for flavouring; she knew how to make healing salves for wounds, and cool herb drinks to allay fevers; and she could embroider rich patterns of flowers and birds on linen; and so she gathered knowledge as a bee sips nectar, and with as little effort.

It so happened, that on a wild and stormy winter's night, a hunter became separated from his companions, and lost his way among the mountain paths; for long he wandered round in circles, until completely lost, and weary with battling with wind and rain, he wrapped his cloak closely around him, and lay down to sleep in a sheltered wood not far from the glen where Deirdre was kept concealed.

When the man woke at first light, he was cold to the marrow of his bones, and stiff and sore from

lying all night on the hard, damp earth. Weak with
lack of food and exhaustion, he began to wander
to and fro, until at last he came on the path
leading up to the fort. Wearily he dragged himself up the steep slope, thinking that here at last
was shelter, and he might go into the rath and
kindle a fire and warm his chilled limbs—when
to his surprise and terror he heard voices and
laughter coming from above.

At first he thought it might be the fairies, and
feared to intrude upon the Good Folk in their
secret kingdom; but presently, as he stood

straining his ears, it seemed to him that these were human voices—so raising his own, he began to call to them for help.

Now when Deirdre first heard the man's voice she said to her foster-mother, "Nurse, what sound is that? For I have never heard its like upon these hills."

Then the nurse answered, "Take no notice, child; it is only some great bird seeking the company of others of its kind, and strayed from the familiar flock."

But after some minutes, receiving no reply, the hunter called again. And again Deirdre asked the woman to tell her what was the meaning of these strange cries, and the nurse said, "Why do you trouble your pretty head with such wonderings —for indeed this is a thing of no account."

But even as she uttered these words, the hunter cried out yet a third time; and on hearing his voice, Deirdre rose up from her stool by the fire, saying, "What you tell me may be true, but I have a fancy to see this great bird, or whatever manner of creature it is." And before the nurse could prevent her, she had unlatched the great bar from the door, and thrown it wide open.

No sooner had she done so than the hunter came towards her, and both stood dumb, staring at each other in amazement.

Then the nurse bustled forward and bade the man enter, for she could see he was foredone with weariness; and her heart being wrung with

fear by the thought of the King's anger should he
hear of the stranger's visit, she thought that the
sooner he had food and rest, and was set upon
his way again, the better for all of them. So she
hastened to put a stool near the fire, and bade
the stranger seat himself, and quickly she brought
out bread, and meat, and a big bowl of mead, and
set them by his side.

But the man sat there as one in a trance gazing upon Deirdre, and she in her turn gazing upon him. And at last he found speech again, and said, "Maiden, great was my weariness and hunger while I waited for the door to open. But now, both are gone from me as I behold your beauty."

Then the nurse came forward hastily and spoke harshly to the man, bidding him to eat and drink, and be gone from the house. "For," said she, "we have better things to do than to sit and listen to your idle chatter; and no good is it for the maiden here to have her head turned by your foolish words."

And the stranger replied, "Dumb I may be if that is the return you ask for your hospitality— but I know of some people in the world who, could they see this rare jewel you keep concealed here, would give their wealth and all else to steal her away."

Then Deirdre spoke for the first time, and said, "And who are these people, stranger, who would wish to take me away from this my home?"

And the man answered, "Well, I can tell you of three, and they are Naoise the son of Uisne, and his two brothers Allain and Ardan."

"And how may we know these if we were to see them?" asked Deirdre.

"I have given you their names," said the man, "and their appearance is thus—tall are they as young pine trees, and black is their hair as a raven's wing. Their skin is white like the foam of the waves, and the blood in their cheeks and lips is scarlet; strong they are as the salmon leaping in the stream, and the stag on the hill, and Naoise is comely above all the other young men of the people of Erin."

Then the nurse spoke in fear and fury, and said to the hunter, "However these young men be, get you gone out of here, and take another road for your way, and may ill fortune follow you for the evil you have done this day."

Then the hunter rose and, bewildered by the woman's words and her evident terror, he went his way. And as he crossed the hills, so his thoughts circled like hungry birds round the maiden, and her blue cloak, and the wonder of her beauty, and the music of her voice. And angered by the harsh words spoken to him, he resolved in his mind to go to Naoise and his brothers and tell them of what he had seen in the glen; and at the first opportunity this is what he did.

Now when the young men had heard his story, they thought at first it was a dream which had fallen on the man because of his exhaustion and hunger. But when he fell to describing Deirdre, her blue cloak, and the colour of her eyes and hair, the delicacy of her hands, her slender feet in their scarlet sandals, and the silver music of her voice, they ceased their doubting, and questioned him more closely as to the exact way to the distant glen. And when he had gone, Naoise said to his brothers, "What is in your minds? Shall we hunt the deer in those parts before many days are sped?"

But Allain, who was ever the cautious one of the three said, "Let us wait a little and see what we can discover of this mystery. For we might draw down upon ourselves the anger of some chieftain, or even of the King."

But Naoise and Ardan threw back their heads, and laughed loudly and long; and both averred that they feared no chieftain, nor yet the King, and it would be worth risking whatsoever might happen if only they could set eyes on Deirdre, and see for themselves if all the hunter had told them was true.

And so it was settled.

But before Naoise and his brothers could carry out their plan, a dispute arose with a neighbouring chieftain, and the young men were called upon to go out with their father's kinsfolk and vassals, and settle the matter with their swords if peaceful words would not avail.

And in the end it came to a sharp tussle, and Allain received a spear thrust in his left thigh, and although the wound was cleansed as well as might be, yet he suffered from a fever, and a little lameness, and so it was some months before he could run again or take part in the chase.

Now one day, while he was sitting before the house in the sun, idly polishing his weapons, and watching Naoise and Ardan wrestling together on the springy turf, a shadow fell across his hands, and he looked up, and saw standing before him the same hunter who had brought news of Deirdre. And after greetings had been exchanged, the man said that he had been visiting kinsfolk near by, and had thought to call in and see if they had gone to the glen to prove for themselves that it was no made-up tale.

And when Allain said no, and told him what had come about since their last meeting, the man said, "One of my kinsmen is man to Connor of the Iron Fist, who dwells near the King's hall, and he has told me somewhat which has a bearing on why the maiden is kept in the distant rath away from men's eyes."

Then Allain called out to Naoise and Ardan to come and hear what the hunter had to tell. And the man said, "Perhaps it is by a lucky stroke of fate that your brother's wound has kept you tied to your home-place, for it seems that there is a prophecy that this maiden, whose name is Deirdre, will bring down much sorrow on Ulster, and cause the death of many heroes. And because of this, King Conchobor has sent her to live in solitude all her days, and no man dare venture near the place for fear of the King's anger."

Then Naoise said in his turn, "It is a cruel fate that so young and beautiful a maiden should have to spend her days in company with an old woman, nor know the companionship of others of her own age. And for my part I am the more eager to see this Deirdre and to risk the King's displeasure."

Then Allain the cautious said, "Gladly would I too see the maiden, but it will be little help to her if the King should hear of our visit, and vent his anger upon us."

And Naoise answered quickly, "Let us slip away secretly, and when we have seen Deirdre and talked to her, we shall know what is best to be done. For my part I am resolved to go." And Ardan said eagerly, "And so am I."

Then the hunter looked from one to another, and said quietly, "You can trust me that never from my lips shall any learn of your venture. But go carefully and without revealing your intent to anyone, for greatly do I fear what may happen if any word of your going comes to the King's ears." So he bade them farewell and went on his way.

And after he had left them they sat together in the twilight and made their plans. And it was decided that they would pretend to be on a visit to some kinsfolk in the south, and go in that direction; but after a time when they deemed it to be safe, they would make a wide circle on their tracks, and find their way to the glen from the far side, and in this way they could hope to be unobserved. And so they talked until the shadows lengthened from the mountains, and night fell suddenly over the land.

K

3. The Meeting
of Deirdre and Naoise

ONE MORNING, very early, when spring held the world in its enchantment, Deirdre and her foster-mother were walking on the hill beyond the fort, rejoicing in the warmth of the sun, and the scent of the air, and the cool feel of the grass beneath their bare feet—for often they would walk thus and dabble their feet in the dews.

They were carrying each a rush basket, for they had in mind to go to a certain sheltered field where small, delicious mushrooms were to be found at this season. The nurse used them to give a flavour to their meat and fish, and to make a certain dish mixed with milk and herbs which Deirdre liked to eat for her supper.

There were primroses, too, in this field, starring all the southern bank with their wondering young faces, and among them grew clumps of early violets. Deirdre liked to pick a great, cool bunch of these, and laying them in her basket covered with fern leaves to keep the sun off them, she would carry them back to the rath. The mushrooms were easy to find, for they sprang up all over the thick, springy turf, and pretty they were to see, with

their delicate pink under-sides, and the dew on their white caps.

So they walked slowly on, with their eyes turning this way and that, exclaiming at the glory of colour everywhere to be seen. Splendid indeed was the sight on which they feasted their eyes. In front of them, on the far horizon, rose the Mountains of Mourne, with their eleven peaks; softly they lay together, with their feet resting among the pine woods below, and great white clouds sailing over their heads; to the left was the sparkling shield of Lough Neagh, and to the right, smaller hills rose in the distance. And in between was the bog myrtle, and the white ribbon of a river threading its way between green banks, and all the twisting paths of the hill country.

Now as they were looking towards the east, what should they see but three small figures winding their way steadily up the steep track through the valley. And the nurse laid a hand on Deirdre's arm, and began to draw her quickly back towards the house, "For," said she, "it is best to keep ourselves hidden until we find what manner of people these be." But there was a dark foreboding in her heart as she remembered the black look the hunter had cast at her in the moment when he had turned and gone from them.

Deirdre too remembered the hunter: but it was his words about the three Sons of Uisne that she called to mind—and a strange excitement troubled her heart at the thought that at last she might set her eyes on Naoise and his brothers. Fear was in the excitement, and pleasure, and a desire to hold back the moment, and yet an eager longing to run forward with open arms into whatever of joy or sorrow the day might bring.

So the two women returned to the rath, and remained indoors, waiting in silence for what might befall. The sunlight pierced in a single shaft of gold through the one small window of the room, and lay on the blue of Deirdre's cloak where she sat by the table, and tangled itself in her hair so that it glittered like silver fire. And there was no sound but the hissing of the turfs on the hearth-stone, and the small creaks from the old nurse's stool as she moved uneasily from time to time. So an hour passed, and then another, but no knock fell upon the door, or voice called in greeting.

At last, weary of suspense, Deirdre rose, and said to the nurse, "No longer will I hide here in the half-dark with the sun shining outside. What harm can come to us from these strangers? Let us go out boldly and welcome them." And so speaking she stooped and latched on her scarlet sandals, and threw open the door.

But no sound of steps fell on her ear, nor of voices echoing up from below—so she ran swiftly to the back of the rath, and shading her eyes, looked down to where they had seen the figures first. And behold—there was no one in sight. Nothing living could she see, but a buzzard wheeling high in the heavens, and two rabbits playing in the grass near by. And suddenly it seemed to her that the sun shone less brightly, and sitting down, she covered her face with her hands and wept.

In the meantime, Naoise and his brothers were lost in the excitement of the chase; for although they had resolved to climb up to the rath, and see if the hunter's story was true, they had been

149

diverted by the sight of a stag which suddenly appeared on a ridge of high ground to their right. There it stood, in all the pride of its strength, its magnificent head held high, so that the great, branching antlers were outlined against the blue of the sky. A moment it stood thus, snuffing the air with distended nostrils, and then it was gone.

All thoughts of the maiden flew out of the young men's minds, and loosing their long-limbed greyhounds, they sprang eagerly after the deer. Long and hard was the chase—and not until late afternoon did they succeed in their endeavour; and after the slaying of the stag they threw themselves down to rest, surrounded by the panting hounds in their crimson collars studded with silver.

It so happened that their course had led them to the banks of a stream which ran through the lonely glen; and having drunk their fill from it and satisfied their hunger with oaten cakes, they began to follow the water which ran merrily round the side of a small wood.

Now when Deirdre had overcome her disappointment at their disappearance, she had risen up, and going indoors had begged from her foster-mother a small loaf and some butter, and milk in an earthen jar—and, saying that she wished to spend the day by the stream in the valley, had gone quickly down the hillside.

The woman felt much uneasiness lest Deirdre should encounter the strangers; but the girl was used to roaming where she would over the fells

and beside the water, and the nurse, sensing her unrest, felt it better to give her her wish—so she let her go unhindered, save that she called after Deirdre to return well before sundown.

And so it happened that when Naoise and his brothers had followed the stream to the other side of the wood they came suddenly upon the maiden, sitting with her feet in the water, and her little scarlet sandals on the grass at her side.

So deep was she in thought that she did not at first notice their approach, but one of the hounds, running ahead of the rest, reached Deirdre, and with his long, sensitive tongue gently licked her hand. At once she sprang up with a low cry—then fell silent as she saw the three young men standing

before her. And as she looked, she saw that the hunter's words regarding them were true—for tall they were all three, and white, and red, and black in colouring, and splendid in their young manhood.

Naoise wore a cloak of deep green with a silver clasp, richly chased. His tunic was of soft gold, and green thongs were wound round his shapely legs, and his feet were shod in sandals of deerskin. On his left arm were two broad bands of gold, and he wore a golden collar round his neck. In his right hand he carried a long and fine green spear. All this Deirdre saw as she stood silent in a torment of shyness.

But now Naoise stepped forward, and taking Deirdre by the hand, he drew her towards him, and gently gave her the kiss of greeting on either cheek —and so did she in return; and Allain and Ardan gave her their salutes—and when it was over the maiden's face was as rosy as a summer's dawn with fiery blushes, for she was of a modest and delicate nature.

Then at last Naoise found voice, and said, "I think you are the maiden of whom we have heard, although indeed, such is your beauty, that I took you to be one of the Children of Danann, the Immortals."

And she replied, "I am Deirdre—and you, I think, are Naoise the Son of Uisne, and these are your brothers."

Then as he looked upon her, standing before him like a brilliant bird or a moving star, the heart of Naoise leaped in his breast like a young salmon leaping in a river, and in that moment he gave to Deirdre a love that he gave to no living creature, nor to any bright vision, but to her alone. And impetuously he burst forth, "O Deirdre, a cruel wrong it is that you should be imprisoned in these lonely hills with none but the birds and beasts for your companions."

And Deirdre answered, "It is not by my will that matters are thus with me. But my nurse has told me that it is by the order of King Conchobor that I am kept here; for in some manner my parents had roused his anger, and this is his revenge, that I must spend all my days hidden from the eyes of men."

Then the brothers together cried out in anger and pity—and Naoise said, "O Deirdre, would that I could succour and defend you against the King's anger."

And Deirdre laughed, and putting her hand on Naoise's shoulder, she said, "With you to defend me, O Naoise, I would fear no one. Had I a brother or a friend like you, I should not need to tremble at the King's wrath, or dread his displeasure. So, I call upon you to protect me, Naoise, Son of Uisne, and to release me from this captivity."

For a moment Naoise stood uncertainly, remembering that Conchobor's arm was long, that his memory never failed, and that his sword was sharp-edged—but looking again upon Deirdre, he forgot the whole world, and answered her, "O Deirdre, my heart's queen, now am I your vassal, and all my heart is yours. And if you will trust yourself to me, I will carry you far from these shores to a safe place, and there no harm shall touch you. And this I vow. But I counsel you, say no word of this to your foster-mother, for in her fear of the King she might find means to thwart us, so do not give her your confidence in this."

Then after some further words they parted for that day, and the young men went swiftly back down the mountain paths, keeping to the shelter of the woods when they reached them lest any eyes might note their presence and take word to Conchobor.

And Deirdre climbed slowly up to the rath, the setting sun enfolding her in a misty light, and making a golden path among the rocks.

4. The Flight

Now ALL the days passed for Deirdre like a waking dream; and each one seemed like some rare jewel, holding in its heart the brilliant secret of Naoise, Son of Uisne.

The foster-mother noticed how dreamy and silent Deirdre had become—how she spent long hours wandering among the hills, and sometimes had to be spoken to three or four times before she answered. But as the days went on, and nothing more was seen or heard of the three strangers, the woman thought that it was the spring weather which caused Deirdre's strange moods—and decided not to speak on the matter.

So Deirdre waited; for Naoise had told her before they parted that he would have to make many preparations for their journey, and these must be made with care, lest the least hint of their going should take root in men's minds. And so she must be patient, and have no fears, but to watch the little wood—and in particular, one small birch tree standing on the bend of the stream, for there he would put a sign on his return.

And at last one day when she went down the path, and turned aside to climb on to the rock from which she could see that corner of the wood, she saw a small crimson cloth waving from one of the branches—and knew that Naoise was there with his brothers.

Wildly her heart throbbed with joy as she climbed back to the rath—but she forced herself to go in quietly, and put on her sandals slowly, and to fasten her blue cloak firmly with the great silver clasp which her nurse had told her was a gift from the mother she had never seen—just as her golden armlet came from her father, Colum the Harper.

Then she picked up her little wicker basket, filled with oaten cakes and a jar of honey, and told her foster-mother that she would be out all day on the hills. The woman nodded calmly, for this was a common tale, and told her not to be late for supper—and so they kissed and parted.

Swiftly and lightly Deirdre's small, slender feet carried her down the winding path until she reached the wood; and as she stepped round the bend in the stream, Naoise and his brothers behind him came to meet her.

Softly they kissed, and then, holding her hand firmly in his strong brown one, Naoise drew her into the shelter of the wood, and made her seat herself on the mossy outflung roots of a great tree, while the young men sat or lay on the ground before her. Then, in his quiet, deep voice he began to talk.

"It is in my mind, Deirdre, that I must take you into a far place, because the arm of Conchobor is long, and sore is his anger—so we have made ready to go to Alba, and I have a fine boat waiting in a hidden place and strong horses to carry us to it. Is your heart still set on this resolve, accushla?"

And Deirdre answered eagerly and with no hesitation, "O Naoise, son of Uisne, gladly will I go with you to the world's end—for much as I love these hills and my native land, even more do I long for freedom, and the laughter of young companions, and to be free for ever of the King's hatred."

Then Naoise rose, and sat beside Deirdre, and again taking her hand in his, he said very gently, "Happy I am to hear your words, my lovely one. Yet I must ask you to give me a further proof of your trust in me—will you come now, this moment, and let my brothers and me guide you to safety?"

Then Deirdre looked from one to the other of the three faces watching her so tenderly, and she cried out sharply, "But my nurse—my dear old nurse who has been mother and friend to me all my known years! Shall I not even stay to bid her farewell?"

And Naoise answered, "Hard it is for us to leave those we love, but it is best this way. For we dare not risk taking her with us, old as she is, and the need for haste being so great. And if she does not know of your going the King's wrath will not fall so heavily on her when he discovers that you are gone. For you have told us that the woman Laborcham only visits you twice a year, in the early summer and the autumn, so that it is yet some weeks to her coming. Sorry I am to ask this of you, my queen, but I can see no other way to be sure of our escaping unhindered."

Silent Deirdre sat for some minutes, with her eyes looking down—and when she raised them again the young men saw they were filled with tears; but proudly she stood up, and wiping them away with her hand she said, "If this is what you think right, O Naoise, then I will do as you ask. Only be patient with me, for now I have trusted myself wholly to you three, and there can be no going back once we leave this place," and she looked straightly at Naoise and his brothers.

Then all three stooped before her, and each in turn took her hand, and kissed it, and swore to cherish and protect her while life remained to them.

So Deirdre set out on her long journey to Alba, which we call Scotland.

Through the rest of that day, and the long night, they travelled, with the horses' hooves muffled in cloth to deaden the sound, and Deirdre carried in the arms of Naoise. They had brought a spare horse because of the extra burden, and Naoise changed his mount at intervals, and so the horses kept fresh.

So they journeyed under the light of the stars, through lonely valleys, and over darkened plains, and by small lakes, whose reeds, rustling in the

night wind, made a desolate sound—until at length the darkness paled to a faint, pearly grey, and that in turn gave way to long streaks of golden light which filled the eastern sky, and the sun rose before them in all his glory. Then, drawing rein, they rested awhile to eat and drink, and to ease the stiffness from their limbs.

But soon they mounted again and pressed swiftly on, and all that day, and the next too they rode steadily, pausing only to eat and drink, and to walk a little to and fro.

Lovely was the countryside in the warm, spring weather—the young bracken springing close-fisted from the earth, the patches of vivid green which gave warning of the treacherous bogs to those who knew the signs, the dark brown of the peat hags, and the golden-brown of the streams. Always, no matter whether they travelled through the heather, or over field paths, there was the laughter of running water—for that, more than any other is Erin's voice.

And the air was full of the scent of flower, and leaf, and springing grass, and athrob with the gladness of bird-song. And Deirdre looked around her in amazed delight as the changing scenes flitted before them—and her heart leapt with the joy of youth and happiness, and pleasure in the swift movement of the horses, and above all, in newly-awakened love for Naoise.

On the third day at dusk they dismounted, and camped in a little dell, through which a deep, merry stream chattered on its way—and behind some rocks they kindled a small fire, and caught fish in the stream, and Naoise cooked them in the hot ashes, wrapped in leaves and grasses. These they ate with oaten cakes, and quenched their thirst with the clear, fresh water, and then they slept, with one of the brothers keeping watch; and so the three young men took turns to guard Deirdre through the hours of darkness, until a faint tremor of light in the east heralded the dawn. Then they stamped out the remains of the fire, and scattered the ashes, and mounted, and rode forward again.

So the hours passed until Deirdre stirred from a half sleep in Naoise's strong arms, and asked, "What is that deep, roaring sound which beats on the air so steadily, and what is this scent which is new to me, and delicious to breathe?"

And the three answered together, "It is the sea you can hear and smell, Deirdre, and this part of our journey is nearly done."

Before long they came in sight of the great blue-green expanse of water, the small waves sparkling in the sunlight, and the seabirds wheeling and crying over the rocks and sandy bays; and ever the sea itself, spreading to the far horizon so that the eye was lost in its restless, lovely movement.

Then they rode carefully down a narrow, stony track, with the gorse bushes blazing golden on all sides, and the bees singing among the blossoms, and the small linnets flying around them in a charm of song.

And before many minutes they came out into a little creek, or inlet of the coast, and here the waters ran smoothly and quietly, and only made small, dreamy sounds of lapping on the smooth stones of the shore.

Then they dismounted, and Allain held up his arms for Deirdre, and took her gently from Naoise, and set her down in a firm place. And when Naoise had leapt down beside her, he said, "Now you may be at ease, beloved, for here we are on my father's lands, and none will molest us. But it is best that we rest through the hours of the day, for I have arranged that Padric, our father's horse-keeper, should come down to this spot each evening and await our coming. And he will take the horses, and help us launch the boat."

So that day too was peaceful, and Deirdre walked on the shore, and marvelled at the tiny shells, tinted with rainbow colours, and made herself a bracelet of the green, pink and dark brown sea-weed; and Naoise and his brothers watched her, and took pleasure in her joy.

But at length evening crept over the cliffs, and the air began to freshen; and at a nod from Naoise, Ardan put his fingers to his mouth, and gave a long, clear whistle, and then another— and suddenly two bushes behind them moved and parted, and a little man ran out, and came quickly down to where the four stood waiting.

Naoise said to Deirdre, "This is Padric—see, he has brought my hounds, Bran and Finnuala, to help us with the hunting when we come to land again."

Then Allain and Padric walked down the creek a little way, and with Ardan to help them they slowly pushed a long, black boat out of the shelter of some tall sea grasses, and launched it on the water; and with eager cries the hounds sprang on board, and stood sniffing the air in ecstasy.

And Naoise picked up Deirdre once again, and stepped over the side of the boat while the other three held it steady, and put her gently down on a seat in the stern. And hard and fast the four men worked to unfurl the snowy sail, for the wind blew fresh and strong off the shore.

When it was all ready, and Padric had shown them the food and drink he had stored ready for them, he bade them farewell and good fortune, and sprang back to the land. And quickly Naoise and his brothers took up the oars and pulled until the wind caught the sail, and the boat's prow bit into the waves, and she moved forward, exulting in her freedom, the water parting before her, and surging past her sides, while a foamy wake spread fast behind her. And so the south-west wind drove them steadily towards Alba's shores.

5. The Happy Years

ON AND on went the black boat, while the days passed, one like another, until on the third day they saw land ahead. Steadily the purple bar on the skyline grew bigger, and Naoise bade his brothers stir themselves, and help him with the sail—and so the boat swung over, and presently they were moving along with the land on their left.

Then Deirdre, who was up in the bows with Naoise, asked him if this was their destination, and he answered that it was not, they must go on for another two days; and so it was.

But now there was change around them, and ever as the boat fled before the following wind they had glimpses of land, for they had left that first coast behind them, and the new coast was to their left side—long, fierce fangs of rock running down, black and glistening into the water, with the surf boiling around them, and a roaring louder than a hundred lions.

Some islands they passed too, but saw no living creature but the sea-birds, which screamed and whirled around the boat, beating the air with strong wings, and making their ceaseless patterns against the deep, cloud-flecked blue of the sky.

Then at first light on the fifth morning, Deirdre awoke from sleep to feel the boat swinging sharply —and sitting up, wrapped in her warm, blue cloak, she saw that they were passing between two long necks of land. Great pine forests swept down almost to the water's edge, and the scent of them mingled with the salty air—and flocks of wood-pigeons flew above the tops of the trees, and out over the loch.

After a time the wind slackened, and the young men got out the oars again, and pulled strongly with the tide. And gradually, as the day wore on, the water narrowed, and at last they saw land ahead, as well as on either side—and Naoise smiled at Deirdre, and said, "Look well, accushla, for here we will make our home; and it is my wish that you should know happiness in this peaceful glen. Lonely it is, but you can be free of the hills, and go where you will, and there will be kindly folk to welcome you; and always we three shall be there to do your bidding."

And so, safe from pursuit, they came to a quiet shore.

There, in a sheltered place at the head of the glen, stood a small wooden house, stoutly built of pine-wood. The mountains towered up on all sides, blue as the velvety bloom on grapes, and a deep purple in the evenings with the shadows on them.

There was a clear space of turfy green before the house, and a small path, winding down to the

loch's edge. And all night long there was the
sound of the wind singing in the pines, and the
little waves lapping on the shore, and the cries of
the night birds.

The house faced east, and on the south side, in
a little plot of garden, Naoise and his brothers
planted four young apple trees for Deirdre's
delight—and there she learned to grow a few
simple hardy flowers and herbs.

So the days and years passed in tranquil happiness. When the morning light beckoned from the
east, and called them from their sleep, the young
men went out with horns and weapons to the chase,

and with their swift hounds ran down the brown-coated deer, and slew many a great antlered stag. Day after day they pursued the game through wooded heights, and along the mountain sides, exulting in their youth and strength.

And at evening, laden with their spoils, they returned to lay them at Deirdre's feet, and to hear her words of praise and welcome.

When they were not hunting, their delight was to sit by Deirdre, and hear the music of her voice, mingling with the voice of the little waterfall which ran close to their door, filling the air at times with a rainbow-tinted spray, and rippling softly down the glen to meet the loch.

Or sometimes Deirdre would sing to them, songs which her foster-mother had sung to her as a child; and the young men lay on the warm earth, and cleaned their weapons in readiness for the next day—and a deep enchantment was theirs in this simple life.

In all the years there had never been a word of estrangement or bitterness between the four, nor had Naoise or his brothers reproached Deirdre for having separated them from their kinsfolk and friends.

And though the glen was isolated, and far from any town, yet there were people too to share their lives—friendly folk had their homes in little stone cottages hidden in sheltered places. In these houses Deirdre and her companions were always welcome—wherever she went she was beloved for her simplicity and goodness of heart. Children learned to look for her coming, and would run to meet her with loud cries of welcome, and clinging to her hands and her cloak, they would tell her all their secrets, and confide to her in their griefs.

The women gave her plants from their small garden plots, and taught her new ways of cooking fish and meat and oaten cakes, and showed her the use of their mountain herbs and berries.

And the men, simple fishermen, shepherds, hunters, were her servants and protectors one and all, and each in his inmost heart marvelled at her wondrous beauty—and brought her their gifts of food and tree and flower, and sometimes tiny figures of animals and birds carved out of wood to give her pleasure.

Sometimes she would spend a day on the loch with one of these kind-hearted crofters, and while he caught the fish, Deirdre would sit watching the movement of the water, or the reflection of the trees, or gaze at the mountains so high and remote above them. And once her companion bade her look up, and she saw a great bird, turning in slow majestic circles over their heads, rising ever higher and higher until it became a mere speck in the vast canopy of heaven—and the man told her it was an eagle, the great golden eagle which has its eyrie in the highest and most inaccessible peaks. And he told her also how the shepherds dreaded to see these fierce birds flying overhead at lambing time, for they would swoop down, and snatch

up a lamb in their talons, and carry it off to feed
their young.

So Deirdre passed her time in innocent enjoy-
ment.

"I have a hut in a wood; ...
   an ash tree closes it on one side,
   and a hazel, like a great tree by a rath, on the
      other.

   Choice wells are there and waterfalls (good to
      drink)
   they gush forth in plenty;
   Berries of yew, bird-cherry and privet are
      there.

   Produce of mountain ash, black sloes from a
      dark blackthorn,
   Berry fruits, bare fruits ...

   A clutch of eggs, honey, mast
   and heathpease sent by God,
   Sweet apples, red cranberries, whortleberries.

   Beer and herbs, a patch of strawberries,
   (Good to taste in their plenty)
   Haws, yew-berries, nut-kernels.

   A cup of excellent hazel mead, swiftly served;
   brown acorns, masses of bramble
   with good blackberries;

Notes of gleaming-breasted pigeons
(a beloved movement),
The song of a pleasant constant thrush above
    my house;

Bees, chafers (restricted humming, tenuous
    buzz);
barnacle geese, brent geese, shortly before
    Samain
(Music of a dark wild one);

A nimble linnet, active brown wizard,
from the hazel bough; there with pied plumage
are woodpeckers . . .

Fair white birds come, herons, gulls . . .
the sea sings to them; not mournful
is the music made by dun grouse from russet
    heather."

Small wonder was it that the years sped by as in
a dream, and Deirdre grew ever more beautiful,
so that her beauty filled the little house with
radiance, and the hearts of Naoise and Allain and
Ardan rejoiced in it with a keen rapture.

And so, for this short spell, the gods smiled
upon them.

6. The Messenger

TERRIBLE HAD been Conchobor's anger when word was brought to him by Laborcham that Deirdre was gone, none knew how or where. Well was it for the old nurse that she had chosen to stay in the rath rather than face the King's fury; but Laborcham had believed the foster-mother's tale, and told Conchobor that she was sure the woman had no inkling of her charge's flight. For the nurse had been too terrified to mention the hunter and his threat to tell the Sons of Uisne about Deirdre.

But as time went on and no news of the fugitives came to light the matter might have been forgotten by all save the King had it not been for Naoise and his brothers; for these three were well-known heroes and fighting-men, and apart from that, they were distantly related to Conchobor himself, through his father's brother's wife.

And so, presently, their absence began to be noticed—and then there were questions, and finally the matter came to the ears of Conchobor, and the King decided to question some of Uisne's vassals. So he sent for them to come to his court, and they dared not disobey the royal summons, and when they were come before Conchobor, he

asked them straightly if they knew of the where-abouts of Naoise and his two brothers.

At first the men were loth to answer, but when it became obvious that no denials or evasions would serve, they admitted that the sons of Uisne were gone to Alba; and further questionings revealed that they had not returned to visit their native land in all these past years. Once this tale was told, it was easy for Conchobor to guess at the truth, and by threatening a horrible vengeance to fall on the kinsfolk of Naoise, and of the men themselves if all were not told, he learned that they were living in the Glen Etive, on the shores of the Loch, and that the maiden Deirdre was with them, and wedded to Naoise.

So angry was Conchobor, that he was unable to speak more with the men, so he sent them back to their own place, and for many days he brooded in silent fury, debating within himself on what to do to get Deirdre into his hands again.

But presently, when the black darkness of wrath had lifted a little from his mind, he could see that it would serve his ends best to appear to accept the whole adventure, and say no words about ven-geance—but try to find some way of persuading the young chiefs to bring Deirdre back to Ulster.

Long he considered the matter, making one plan after another, and discarding each in turn, for underneath his appearance of frankness and honesty, he was a devious and cunning hypocrite, and one who never forgot or forgave any betrayal of his own royalty.

At last he sent for Fergus, his father's brother —he whose wife was kin to the Sons of Uisne— and said to him, "It has come to my ears, my uncle, that Naoise the son of Uisne and Allain and Ardan his brothers are living in exile in the land of Alba, and that they have with them the maiden Deirdre, and that she is wedded to Naoise. Now perchance in this way the curse may be lifted from her—and we may cease to fear the anger of the gods. Pity it is that these heroes should live exiled from their native land, and a loss to us is their strength if war should come. Give me your advice, my uncle, for I have always relied on your wisdom."

Then Fergus answered, "True are your words, O Conchobor. And indeed there has been much talk of Naoise and his brothers among the knights, and many wish for their return to Erin. It seems to me that if you were to choose three young men as their sureties, you could send a messenger to Alba, and assure the Sons of Uisne that if they return to Ulster no harm will come to them, or to the maiden Deirdre—and the lives of the sureties will stand for the truth of your promises."

And this plan seemed a good one to Conchobor, so he agreed to all Fergus said; and the three young men chosen were Cormac, son to Conchobor, Fiacra, son of Fergus, and Dubthach, son of a great chieftain; and Conchobor asked Fergus himself to journey to Alba, and seek out the Sons of Uisne, and persuade them to return to Erin. For well he knew that a long friendship lay between Fergus and those three. And so it was decided.

Thus it came about that one evening, when the sun was getting low, and shadows were falling across the mountains, and the sky was flushed like a flame, and the colour reflected back from the water in the softness of a dog-rose's petals— Deirdre and Naoise sat within the doorway, and played their game on a shining silver board with golden men; and Allain and Ardan polished their spears and looked on.

And as they played, suddenly Bran got to his feet from where he was lying at Deirdre's side, and threw up his head, and sniffed the air, and broke into a deep barking, which echoed like a bronze bell round the loch. Now as they all listened, they heard a distant shout over the water, and Naoise sprang up, overturning the board so that all the golden pieces were scattered on the floor, and so did Allain and Ardan, and Naoise said, "A man of Erin gave that call." And at his words, a cold fear fell on Deirdre's heart—a chill wind shrivelled her spirit, as if for a moment the wing of Fate hovered over the small house, and blotted out the light. And slowly, she too rose to her feet.

Then once again, the cry rang out—and it was a man's voice, clear and strong: and Naoise said joyfully to his brothers, "I know that call; it is

Fergus, our old friend and chieftain. He has come from Erin to see how we fare—no harm is in the visit. Let us go down and give him welcome."

Then Deirdre laid her hand on Naoise's arm, and begged him in a low voice to turn a deaf ear to what Fergus might say—"For," said she, "I fear that he has come from Conchobor, and danger accompanies him. Last night I dreamed an evil dream. Three great birds flew down, and brought honey in their beaks—but when they flew away they took each three drops of our heart's blood. And this dream is an omen, and a warning to beware of the King's honeyed words, for behind them lies treachery and death."

Then Allain and Ardan looked troubled, but Naoise smiled, and answered gently, "It grieves me that your sleep should be troubled in this manner. But have no fears, pulse of my heart, for never would Fergus consent to bear a false message. We have known him from our boyhood, and he is staunch and true. For my sake come down with us and greet him kindly."

But Deirdre, seeing that at that time she could do no more, bade them go before her, as she must pick up the golden men from the ground where they had fallen, and put away the silver board; for in her heart she felt she must have a little longer before she could meet Fergus with a smiling face. So the young men started down to the shore, with the great grey hounds leaping before them—and loud was their joyous greeting of Fergus, as his long boat was rowed slowly towards them. But Deirdre stood desolate in the doorway, trying to overcome her dread.

Merrily that evening went by, with jests, and laughter, and the deep music of men's voices speaking together. For Deirdre brought out such simple fare as they had, venison, oaten cakes, honey, and put them in the eating place, and mead in plenty stood in the drinking place, and long the heroes sat there, hearing the news of home, and answering each other's questions.

But as the night wore on the laughter ceased, and Fergus stood up from his seat, and looking round the circle of faces in the firelight, he spoke.

"O Deirdre, and you, Sons of Uisne," he said, "good it has been to sit here with you, and talk of home and past days. But now I must speak of my embassy—for I have a message for you from Conchobor and his knights, and it is for this I am come. For he sends greetings to you, and would have me say that he no longer bears malice in his heart towards you because of your deed in stealing Deirdre out of his care. And it is his desire that you should all four return to Ulster, and settle once more among your own people. And that you may feel able to trust in his words, he bids me say that he has chosen three sureties, whose lives will be forfeit should any offer you violence—and of these three, one is his own son Cormac, and there is my son Fiacra, and your old comrade Dubthach."

So he ceased from speaking and sat down, and strong and true was his face in the firelight, with the gleam of the silver in his beard, and the steady eyes.

But before Naoise and his brothers could answer, Deirdre sprang to her feet—and the light shone in beauty on her fair hair, and was reflected from the silver clasp of her tunic, and she cried in her glorious voice, "O Naoise, and you, Allain and Ardan, I beg you to heed me, for the words of your kinsman fill my heart with dread. Never would I wish to show lack of courtesy to any under this roof—but I have warning within that great evil will fall upon us all if you accept the King's offer. As you love me, do not go, but let us remain here in peace."

Then Naoise also rose, and went to her side, and took her hand, speaking gently and caressingly.

"Heart of my heart, it is understandable that you should feel thus, and wonder if Conchobor's wrath can be so easily forgotten—but here is a fair offer brought by one we would all three trust with our lives. And happy as we are here, it is an ill thing to live so far from our own folk, and our native land. If the King is willing to forgive us what have we to fear? Amongst our own people there are strong arms and good friends, and you will always have us by your side to protect you."

And Fergus added his persuasions to those of Naoise, and so did the other two. And seeing that their minds were already made up, Deirdre

refrained from further speech that night. But while the men talked eagerly of the future, and made plans for a speedy departure, Deirdre sat back in the shadows, and wept silently, the tears falling one by one down her lovely face and onto her hands lying quiet in her lap—but no sound escaped her lips. And she remembered how Naoise had told her that Conchobor was not one to forget an injury, and that it was safest to put the wide seas between themselves and his anger.

And presently she rose, and slipped out into the starlight, unnoticed save by the two faithful hounds, who followed silently at her heels—and her feet carried her down the familiar path to the loch's edge. Once there she sat herself on the stones, still faintly warmed from the sun's rays, and gave herself up to her thoughts, for her heart was filled with sorrow, and a fore-knowledge of ill in the days to come, and the hounds lay one on each side of her.

So she looked back in her mind down the past days and years, and remembered all the happiness she had known with the Sons of Uisne in the glen, and the kindness of neighbours, and the love of the little children.

And after a long while she rose, and went slowly back up the path to the house—but before she went indoors again, she found her way in the darkness to her beloved apple trees, and putting out her hand, she tenderly stroked the rough, firm young trunk of each in turn, and whispered a farewell.

And so the happy years were ended.

7. The Return

FEW DAYS were left then before the long, black boat was launched again—days of exultant joy for Naoise and his brothers, and for Deirdre, days precious as rare jewels, yet like the briar-rose studded with sharp thorns.

Sadly her feet carried her from one loved spot to another—wistfully she gazed at the great blue mountain peaks, and watched the shadows dancing over the fells as the buzzards flew screaming between her eyes and the sun.

But now her grief was too deep for tears, and her pride forbade her to show any sign of the cloud which lay like night over her spirit.

Fergus had gone again the day after his coming, to bear the news of their return to Conchobor and all the knights of the Red Branch. But he left three of his men behind to help sail the boat, and glad were Naoise and his brothers to have hands to speed on the preparations for departure.

All too soon then that day came for Deirdre—the boat was loaded with gear and the needful food and drink. Now the little house stood empty, forlorn against their going. It was autumn, and everywhere the heather flung its proud purple banner—and blazing crimson were the berries on the rowan trees, and the leaves of the brambles. But, as if even the skies knew of Deirdre's sorrow, a soft grey cloud lay over the water—and the loch itself showed dark as steel. Even the wood-pigeons were silent, and a sombre hush lay over the woods.

In silence too the little group climbed into the boat, and took their places. Deirdre wrapped her cloak closely around her, and now and then her hand went up to touch the little spray of heather and the few late blooms picked from her cherished garden, and pinned to her breast with the great silver clasp.

Quietly Naoise came and took his seat at her side, and laid a hand on hers—deep and flowering was the love between these two, a marvel to see— and his heart was sore for her. Yet this was their fate that they should leave happiness behind, and go forward into peril and darkness.

Slowly at first, then faster the boat moved into the centre of the loch, the dip of the oars the only sound to break the stillness, and so they left Alba for ever.

For three days the boat ran swiftly down the rocky coasts, and breasted the waves in eager pride, her sail belling out before the wind like a swan's wing.

But on the fourth day the wind changed, and blew strongly against them—and there was an ugly swell on the waters, and the boat began to pitch heavily and roll to and fro in torment. Hard was

it to hold her on her course, and the oars came out, and the men took turns in rowing and steering—but they made little headway that day.

It was a black night with no stars, and a feeling of doom in the darkness, and the boat moved sluggishly as if she was reluctant to go forward. Every now and then a wave, bigger than the others, would break over the bows, and despite all they could do, they were soon soaked and miserable.

Dawn came, bringing no improvement. They stared out over a tumbling waste of sullen, grey waters, topped here and there with white caps. The waves slapped angrily against the boat's side and the skies, lowering and grim, seemed to come down to meet the seas.

184

Naoise spoke words of comfort to Deirdre, saying, "Have no fears, pulse of my soul—worse storms than this have I seen. Our boat is stout and willing—delayed we may be, but we shall yet come safely to shore."

And she answered, "Where you are, O beloved, I am happy—nor do I fear wind and water, for they are familiar friends even in their anger."

But in her heart she thought this storm to be an omen of disaster, and a warning to turn back while there was time. But no word of this passed her lips.

It was a little past noon when one of the men gave a shout and pointed to the north—and they saw a dark, steel-blue line of cloud stretching across the horizon. The wind dropped, and there was an ominous calm, but the waters continued to be troubled. They set to work to lower the sail, for Allain said that there was a worse gale to come, and it would soon be torn from the mast. Having done this, they could do no more. Nor had they long to wait. With a scream like ten thousand fiends the storm was upon them—they could not speak for the clamour of the wind, nor see for the spray which blew all about them.

The boat plunged heavily down into the trough of the great waves, and climbed slowly up out of the abyss like a wounded creature struggling for life. Then the heavens opened—and hail came hissing and stinging into the boat, cutting their faces with sharp points, and covering all with a white cloak as if it were mid-winter. Thunder roared amidst the roaring wind—dazzling were the lightning flashes, and black as a pit was the sky above them. Now the boat swung round, in spite of all their efforts, and raced madly before the wind—fleeing like a stricken bird driven onwards by the fury of the elements.

So time passed, no one knew how, or why, or whether it was still daylight, or if the sun had long set. Their ears were deafened with the ceaseless roaring, and their eyes blinded by the lightning and salty spray. So the storm raged for a day and a night—and when its fury was spent, they found they were blown far off their course with no land in sight, and their food and water running low. All were bruised and shaken, one of Fergus's men had a broken arm; and weary they were beyond telling, and disheartened too.

The wind had dropped, but there was still a stiff breeze blowing, and although they did their utmost, they were unable to hoist the sail that day. The boat was wallowing heavily with all the water she had taken in-board, and they had to waste their little energy in baling it out as best they might.

But at evening they managed to pull the boat back on her proper track, and to hoist the sail again—and now, as if the storm gods were sorry for their spite, the skies cleared, and the rays of the sinking sun stretched out across the sea, making a radiant path of gold into which they sailed. The colour of the water changed to a lovely turquoise blue, and gulls appeared suddenly and flew over their heads, as if to give them courage and good cheer.

So they sailed for another day, and then, faint and misty as a hyacinth, they saw the land rising out of the sea—first only a small speck in the distance, and then as big as a man's arm outstretched. And the colour deepened, and turned to violet and green, and they knew that the end of the voyage was in sight.

Swiftly now, and with a kindly breeze to aid them, they drew ever nearer to the shores of Erin, until the dear familiar landmarks were clearly to be seen.

Steadily the boat moved onward, held by the strong impetuous waves. And as they looked ahead the deep, velvety blue heads of the Mourne Mountains looked down upon them—and the scents of land drifted out to greet them, mingled scents of gorse, honey-sweet, and heather and the reek of turf smoke.

Then Naoise spoke above the sound of the waves, and Deirdre turned her head to look at his beloved face, for she knew each small movement and gesture, and his voice was dear to her above all others.

"Now the gods have been kind to us, and brought us through the fierce anger of the storm to our native shores. What is to come we know not, but it is a happy thing to smell the sweet air of our own country, and to hear familiar voices again, and to know our own folk have not forgotten us. Let us be glad in this day, and thank the gods for the favours they have shown us."

Firmly yet pleadingly he spoke, and his eyes rested on Deirdre and hers on him, and when his speech was ended she smiled, and answered gently as was her wont.

"Happy indeed, O Naoise, are we to come safely to shore, and my heart rejoices in your joy. Lovely is the sight of the hills looking down on us, and smell of the gorse, and the blue smoke rising from the houses of friends. Let us go forward with courage to whatever awaits us."

But under her brave words she hid an increasing terror, for she had the gift of the Sight, and well she knew that nothing but sorrow would come of their trusting to the good faith of King Conchobor.

Then the boat surged forward in one long, proud leap, and her prow bit into the sand. As they stood up, they could see small figures running down the cliff paths to meet them, and heard the distant shouts of welcome. So they came to their own shores.

Glad indeed were the hearts of the travellers as they went forward to meet their kinsfolk and friends—and amongst those who had come to meet them and welcome them home were the three sureties, Cormac, Fiacra and Dubthach.

When the first greetings were over, Cormac said

to Naoise, "My father bade me give you his welcome, and speak words of gladness for your returning. But he had not looked for your coming so soon, and the house he had chosen for your dwelling-place is not made ready. Happy would he have been to welcome you to his own halls, but as you are wedded with the maiden Deirdre, and there has been anger between himself and you on her account, he thought your hearts would be easier to be in your own place. And so I am come to lead you there, that you may rest and eat."

Now when Deirdre heard these words her heart fluttered like a captive bird in its cage, and all her fears came upon her with strength and coldness. For certain she was that there was malice and not friendship behind this speech.

But Naoise only smiled, and said calmly, "You will thank the King your father for his friendly words, and give him our greetings. Weary indeed we are after our days of battling with the seas, and our bodies are longing for sleep."

Then willing hands helped to unload the boat, and Cormac and his friends led the way, and so in a little while they came to a hut standing by itself, and lonely was the place, and dark. But there was a stout door with good bars top and bottom, and pallets covered with skins along the walls, for it was a goodly size, and turfs all ready for lighting on the hearthstone.

Then Cormac said again how sorry Conchobor was that all was not in readiness for them as he would have wished, but it would only be for a few days, and the King would look for their coming after they had rested and thrown off the travel weariness. And he assured Naoise that no harm or violence would be offered to them, and that they might be at ease. And so he left them for that time.

8. The Welcome

WHEN CORMAC and his companions had gone, Deirdre quickly set to work to make some comfort within the house, and Naoise and his brothers helped her as they could. Soon a cheerful blaze brought light to the gloom, and food was set in the eating place, and drink in the drinking place, and so they took their rest. But before they lay down to sleep, Naoise shut the door, and swung the two great bars into place—and spears were put ready to hand, and the heroes' gold-studded shields stood up against the wall. And they took it in turns to keep a watch so that they might not be taken unawares.

Now when they had had their sleep, and were sitting talking together, with the door once more thrown open, Deirdre could hold back no longer from speaking of those things which had troubled her mind since first they came to land. And so, when there was a lull in the talk, she said suddenly, "Strange it seemed to me that your kinsman Fergus did not come down with his son to welcome you, for they would have told us had he met with some mischance or sickness. And you will remember how I said to you before we left Alba's shores, that if Conchobor lodged us in his own halls we could be free of doubts—but this he has not done —so that I fear to trust in his goodwill."

And Ardan said, "I too wondered at his absence." And Naoise and Allain were agreed that surely Fiacra, son of Fergus, would have told them if there had been anything amiss. Then Allain said, "I was not able to believe wholly in Cormac's words, for it seemed to me that they had more the sound of excuses than of friendship." And Ardan added, "Yes, and this is surely a lonely place that has been chosen for our dwelling—for Conchobor might have found us a house nearer to his own halls had he been so glad of our coming." So they decided to wait and see what the next days brought forth, and to keep a strict watch night and day.

In the meantime news had been brought to King Conchobor that Deirdre and the Sons of Uisne were settled in the place he had chosen for them, and his heart leapt with evil joy, for never had he expected to see them fast within his net. But when his son Cormac came, and told how he had spoken with Naoise and his brothers, and how he had repeated his father's welcome to them, Conchobor praised him, and pretended to feel shame that they should have to dwell in such a poor place, for it was not his intention to let Cormac know of his wish to destroy the Sons of Uisne. And said he, "Willingly would I send for them even now, and welcome them to these halls, but I have had word of a dispute between Connor and Fearachar the son of Ro, and I must go and settle it myself. But do you see that Naoise and his companions lack for nothing until my return." For it was in his mind to set them at their ease, that he might the more easily come at them by surprise and destroy them.

But secretly he sent a messenger to try and get a glimpse of Deirdre and bring back word if she was as beautiful as ever. And this man went down to the hut, and waited until darkness fell, and when he thought he could safely venture nearer, he crept across the grassy track, and stooping, put his eye to a crack in the door.

And when he looked, he saw the fire leaping on the hearth, and rushlights burning, and at the table sat Naoise and Deirdre playing a game with a silver board, which sparkled and flashed as they moved the golden men upon it. And the two brothers of Naoise sat one on each side of the hearth with a sharpened spear leaning by their hands.

But when his gaze fell upon Deirdre, he gave a loud gasp—for her beauty was such as he had never known or even dreamt to see. Her hair glistened like spun silver, and her colouring was white and rose, and blue were her eyes with violet shadows beneath them, and long golden eyelashes. She wore a tunic of rich green, with tiny golden leaves embroidered on it, and golden sandals on her feet—and her laughter rang like a chime of silver bells.

Then the man rose from crouching there, and so

N

bewitched was he by the sight of Deirdre, that he moved to another place where there was a hole big enough to put a finger through, and here he could see her even better. And at last, in his wonder and delight, he gave a long sigh—and in that second Naoise looked up, and saw the man's eye shining through the hole, and he took up one of the silver dice and flung hard—and it went through the hole and took the man's eye from his head, and he fled into the night.

And the next day this man came to where King Conchobor had his lodging—and when Conchobor saw the red wound where the man's eye had been, he asked him how the calamity had come about. So the man told him—and when the tale was ended, he said to Conchobor, "But gladly would I have put my other eye to the door and risked blindness to look a while longer on the beauty of Deirdre; but I feared to be slain, so I came away."

Then Conchobor rewarded him, and sent him away—but in his heart he was resolved to win Deirdre for himself and to slay the Sons of Uisne. And this he vowed to do whatever the consequences.

Now when Naoise had flung the dice, his brothers had leapt to their feet, and seized their spears, and would have opened the door, and gone out to seek the intruder. But Naoise forbade them to go—"For," said he, "how do we know how many may be lurking out there in the darkness? And if we open the door, the firelight will make us a target for any who come against us. Let us stay within, and make ready for what may chance."

So they took up their war gear, and prepared themselves, and Naoise took up his battle clothing, and so did his brothers, and they put it on. Beautiful it was to see, for on it were embroidered the figures of birds and beasts, the tiger and griffin, the eagle, the swift hawk, and the venomous serpent. And they took their shields up, and their spears in their hands, and so they watched through the night hours until the dawn.

And when it grew light they unbolted the door, and went out—but there was no one in sight, only a hare washing its face in the morning dew, and two rabbits scuttling for their burrows.

So they thought it was only some wanderer drawn to the lights of the house—and put off their war clothing, and went in to break their fast.

Now King Conchobor could not take his mind from Deirdre, and the description of her beauty brought to him by the man who had lost his eye. But he was not altogether convinced even yet—so he sent for the woman Laborcham, who had known Deirdre from her childhood's days, and when she was come, he said to her, "I want you to go down to the place where the Sons of Uisne have their lodging, and ask to speak with Deirdre, for I have a fancy to know if the maiden is as beautiful as ever. But do not say that I have sent you, but let it seem that your coming is because of the affection you have for the maiden."

So the woman went down boldly in the daylight, and as she approached, she saw Naoise and his brothers sitting outside the house door, polishing their weapons, and Deirdre was standing, with her hand shading her eyes, watching the clouds flying across the face of the hills and over the plain.

Hearing steps, she turned quickly, and when she saw who it was, she came forward, and putting her hands on the woman's shoulders, she gave her the kiss of greeting on either cheek, and said to her companions, "This is Laborcham, King Conchobor's messenger, of whom I have spoken to you." And to the woman she said, "It is good to see a familiar face again—do you come from the King?"

Then Laborcham returned her kisses, and greeted the young men, and they her, as is the custom in those parts, and she said, "No, I do not come from Conchobor; but hearing word in the clachan that you had landed on these shores again, I remembered the times when I used to visit you in the rath, and a longing came over me to know how you fared, and so I am here."

So they all sat together in the sunlight, and talked of happenings in Ulster, and of one thing and another, and she gave them news of some they had known in past days, and presently the woman bade them farewell and went on her way.

And when she was gone, Deirdre said to Naoise and his brothers, "I do not think she told us her real purpose in coming, for I feel that she was sent by Conchobor. And if he has forgiven us for the wrong put upon him, why does he not let my old nurse come and see me, for Laborcham says she is back here with her kinsfolk—and sure I am that she would have been the first to welcome me had some bar not been put in her way?"

The young men too thought that it was strange that the foster-mother did not come, but they would not show their suspicions too clearly lest they frighten Deirdre; so they said that it was too soon yet to make up their minds that any mischief was intended, and if they kept a good watch no harm could come to them.

N*

But Deirdre felt again the shadow of foreboding, and it was as if a thorn hedge grew up around them, invisible but sharp, and there was no way to get through it. And she thought of her four young apple trees, and the peace of their dear home in Alba, and wept within her heart.

And the woman Laborcham went back to King Conchobor and told him that the beauty of Deirdre was a thing beyond the power of any mortal to describe, and she was lovely as one of the Children of Danann. And when he heard her words he was more than ever resolved to take Deirdre for himself, and to rid himself of the Sons of Uisne in one way or another—and so he sent for the man who was leader of his mercenaries, and between them they made up a plan that was not to be known to any but themselves. And as these men were hired warriors, and not known to the Sons of Uisne, it would be an easy matter to kindle the anger of the young men and provoke them to a fight before their own clansmen could rally to their aid. And it was left to the leader of this band to settle with the men how and when they could put their plan into action; and it was made clear to this man that none of the three brothers were to escape alive.

And so the Druid's prophecy began to take shape and form at last.

9. The First Attack

In this way a week went by, and during that time some of Naoise's vassals came and encamped in a clearing at a little distance from the hut—and friends and kinsfolk also came to greet them and show their gladness at the return of the Sons of Uisne.

Wonderful for that time was the golden autumn weather, with the sunlight brilliantly reflected in the rich blues and purples of the hills, in the vivid golds and crimsons of leaves and berries, and the orange flame of bracken, and flashing back in silver light from the sparkling loch, and the ever-changing colours of the sea. The days were warm and pleasant, and when evening fell a touch of early frost made a keenness in the air, and the sky was lit by that light only to be seen in Erin at twilight, the clear, translucent green of cool waters, and against it trees and hills stood out black and sharp and lovely to see.

And as Deirdre looked at all this beauty, she longed to take her little rush basket as she had done in her girlhood's days, and wander out alone, or with Naoise and his brothers, and spend long hours in roaming over the hills, or gathering herbs and berries in fields and woods. For now all she might do was to go a little way along the stream and gather such flowers as still remained, and the coloured leaves of brambles, and small mosses and ferns, and bring them to the house so that the sight of them might remind her of the happy care-free hours she had known in Alba.

And the young men too longed to take their weapons and the hounds, and spend their days in hunting the stag on the hills, or fishing in the wide strong rivers—but they feared to go far from their dwelling, lest a strong force set upon them, and in the confusion of battle Deirdre be snatched away. For as the days went on and still no word came from Conchobor asking them to visit his halls, they knew certainly that the King's enmity was still alive; and although they feared nothing for themselves, they felt a great dread lest harm should befall Deirdre, who was the light of their eyes.

Then one morning very early, those in the hut were roused by the sound of tramping feet, and men's voices, and the ring of steel. So Naoise and his brothers put on their war clothing, and took up their weapons in readiness, and all waited in a grim silence for what might befall.

And soon enough a loud knock fell on the door, and then it shook as if a heavy weight were thrust against it. And Naoise called out loudly, "Who is there without? And why do you disturb us from our rest? Get you gone or I will come out and hasten your departure."

At this, there were whisperings outside, and

jeering laughter, and a harsh voice called taunt-
ingly, "Come out then, stranger, and give an
account of yourselves, and what you do there
where you have no rights to be."

Then Naoise strode forward, his face black with
fury, and Allain and Ardan at his back, with their

great golden shields held high, and he threw the door open with such force that it clanged against the wall. In the half-light they could see about fifty men, armed with spears and swords; and when they saw Naoise and his brothers, those in the front surged towards the hut, and the leader called, "Now we shall soon see what truth is in your words, stranger, and if you can make good your promise." And with that he lifted his spear, and flung it straight at Naoise.

Then Naoise caught the spear easily on his shield, and the head broke off, so that the useless haft fell to the ground—and he shouted to the men in front of him, "I know not what cause of enmity lies between us, but be sure that if you want a fight we are willing to please you." And with that he and his brothers jumped forward, and keeping close together, thrust so fiercely at the attackers that those in front reeled back under the shock, and threw those behind them into confusion. And then Naoise and Allain and Ardan pressed strongly forward—and loudly rang the sound of steel on steel, and the clash of shield on shield.

So the fight raged to and fro—and many were the wounds given and taken in that hour; fearful indeed were the blows dealt by the heroes, as the sparks flew from the edges of their swords like fiery rain with the heat of the shock, and blood ran like water on all sides, and the ground beneath their feet was so slippery that it was difficult to stand upright.

And within the hut Deirdre stood against the wall, ready to help with the handing out of fresh weapons, and to bind up the wounds later. And she was not idle, for she poured out great beakers of mead to cool the heroes' throats—and linen was fetched out from her store to bandage their hurts, and salves to cool their wounds. And so she waited for the outcome.

Now when the fight had endured for long hours, and many had been slain, and men's breath came fast and hoarse from weariness, the attackers drew off a little, and there was a lull in the fighting and the heroes fell back to the doorway, and stood resting on their shields, ready for what might next befall. But short was this respite, for soon the sound of running feet was heard, and another band of men burst into the clearing, and when the attackers saw them they raised a feeble shout of triumph, and joined the newcomers in a fresh assault. And so for all that afternoon the battle swayed to and fro once more, until men's arms ached with the force of their strokes, and hard was it to endure longer. But Naoise and his brothers fought on without sign of fatigue until, as dusk was falling, a loud shout was heard in the distance, and in a few moments Cormac, Fiacra and Dubthach ran swiftly towards the struggling group, and behind them a number of Naoise's vassals—and they fell on the rear of the attackers, and it was only a matter of minutes before they broke and fled, leaving the dead and wounded behind them.

Then Naoise and his brothers rested from their cruel work—and Deirdre came out to them with mead, and they drank and were refreshed; and when their wounds had been washed and bound up, they went into the hut, and their three sureties came to them—and Naoise said to Cormac, "What is this that has come about, and who has set these men on us to do us an injury?"

And Cormac answered, "I know nothing of the reason for their ill will, O Naoise."

Then Naoise turned to Fiacra and said, "And you, Fiacra, son of Fergus, know you anything of this—and why is it that your father has never come to greet us in all this time?"

And Fiacra answered, "I know nothing, O Naoise—for two of your vassals came running and said that there was fighting around your dwelling, and I sent one of them to tell Cormac, and the other to bring Dubthach, and our hands have been ready in your defence. And my father could not come to greet you because, on his return from Alba, he was put under geasa by a chieftain named Barach to go and partake of a feast with him, and this he might not refuse; yet it seems to me that this may have been of Conchobor's contriving."

Then Naoise looked at Dubthach, and Dubthach spoke out and said, "I know as little as yourselves, Sons of Uisne. Only one thing do I know, that these men who attacked you are Conchobor's men, for I recognised their leader who lies wounded outside."

At his words there was a murmur of astonishment from the others, but Naoise held up his hand, and when they were silent, he turned again to Cormac, and said roughly, "Ill is it on your part to lie to me, son of Conchobor, for you must know that these are your father's men—and what reason is there that we should place any further trust in your promises?"

But Cormac spoke up quickly, and with his face aflame he said to Naoise, "It is true, O Naoise, that I knew these to be my father's hired mercenaries, for I too recognised their leader. And if I did not speak of it at first it was for shame that such a thing were possible—for never would I have believed my father capable of treachery towards you, and my heart is sore within me."

Then Naoise put a hand on his shoulder, and said, "Sorry am I, O Cormac, to have doubted your good faith, and sorry too for your heart's pain, for this is an ill thing, and my brothers and I sorrow for your sorrow. But we are angered too, and never can we forgive this wicked deed, nor feel security again in your father's lands. And it is in my mind to return to Alba."

And Allain and Ardan cried out together, "Yes, let us return to our own place where none will molest us, and live out our lives there in peace, or die in honourable fight, nor see again these treacherous shores." And Deirdre, hearing their words, covered her face with her hands, and wept tears of joy.

Then when the sureties saw that their minds were made up, and that nothing would change their intention, they were overcome with shame and grief, and cried out that they too would leave Erin, or die fighting to save their honour. And Cormac swore to the Sons of Uisne that on his return to his father's halls he would have speech with him, and make it clear that neither he nor the other two sureties would have any part in this treachery—nor would they stand aside and let mischief befall without raising a hand to avert it.

But in spite of their promises Naoise and his brothers again declared their intention of leaving Ulster for ever. "For," said Naoise, "when we took Deirdre away from the cruel imprisonment forced upon her by your father, we swore to her that we would protect her with our lives if need be—and she has no other guardians. Plain it is to see that she cannot dwell here in peace or safety while Conchobor lives, for he will never forgo his vengeance. And now his anger will be the greater because he has failed to destroy us at this time." But he told Cormac and his two friends that if they wished to go with him and his companions to Alba, they on their part would be glad and give them lasting friendship, and to this Allain and Ardan added their assent.

Then seeing that further words were useless, Cormac, Fiacra and Dubthach left the hut; but Cormac said that he would send fifty of his own men to guard the place, and Fiacra promised another fifty of his father's vassals, and Dubthach did likewise. And so they parted for that time.

And when Naoise and his brothers had seen that their vassals stood armed and ready around the house, and were assured that a swift alarm would be given if any danger approached, they withdrew within—and taking off their war clothing, they threw themselves down on their pallets to rest their bruised limbs and weary bodies in readiness for further battle.

And Deirdre busied herself in tending to their needs, and in bringing them food and drink to restore their strength, for they all knew that this day had not brought them to the end of their ordeal, but that there was further malice and sorrow to come.

But while Deirdre went to and fro, occupied with her small tasks, her heart treasured the words of Naoise and his brothers that soon they would all return to Alba and there remain. Her thoughts flew to the little house beside the loch, with the waterfall making its music through the night, and the sighing of the wind in the pines, and the scents from her little garden plot on a warm summer's day, and all the kindly folk who had taken them into their lives and shown them such friendship, and she smiled to think of the children and the welcome they would give her on her return. And so she too lay down to sleep.

10. The Last Battle

WHEN CORMAC and his friends had left the dwelling of the Sons of Uisne, they had gone each one to his own place to choose good and trustworthy men to send to Naoise and his brothers.

Now when this was done, Cormac hurried to the King's house—and when he entered he saw his father standing by the great wood and turf fire in his hall. In his youthful eagerness, Cormac could not wait to greet Conchobor, but burst out hotly, "Ill have you done, my father, to conceal from me your true intent towards the Sons of Uisne. And now I stand shamed before all men's eyes. For your hired mercenaries have failed to slay Naoise and his brothers, and so your evil deed is noised abroad. Moreover, the Sons of Uisne will not forgive your treachery towards them, but are determined to return to Alba and leave Erin for ever. And it is in my heart to go with them, for I can no longer stay under your roof."

Then Conchobor was shaken by a dark anger, and he answered his son thus, "Get you gone out of my sight before I do you an injury—for none shall speak to me as you have spoken and live. The Sons of Uisne stole the maiden Deirdre from my keeping, nor have they repented of their deed. The more fools they to trust me and put themselves in my power. If I cannot bring about their death by this means I will do it by another, and if you turn traitor to your own father, there are others who will not hesitate to do my will."

Then Cormac rushed out of his father's house, and going to his own place he put on his war clothing, and took up his weapons and his heavy shield, and made ready to defend the Sons of Uisne as his promise bound him to do—for well he knew that it would not be long before the King sent a strong band against them. And so it was that before evening came, Cormac and Fiacra and Dubthach and their fighting-men were encamped near the dwelling of Naoise, and prepared to give their lives to save the Sons of Uisne.

Now when Cormac had gone from his father's presence, Conchobor sat alone awhile and debated in his mind what he could do to make sure that the Sons of Uisne were slain, and Deirdre was once again in his power.

And suddenly a most evil thought came to him, and he sent for Connor of the Iron Fist, one of his foremost knights, and told him to go and send a summons to all the knights of the Red Branch to come to the King's house, for he had news of grave import to impart to them.

And when the knights were come, Conchobor bade them enter the hall, and seat themselves on the wooden benches round the great table, and he seated himself in his carved chair, and looked around at them, but for some time he said nothing but sighed heavily, and an uneasy silence hung over all present.

Then at last Conchobor stood up—and splendid he looked in his crimson cloak, and his white linen tunic richly embroidered with intricate patterns—and he began to speak slowly, and as if each word was an effort, and he said, "I have called you all here because it is necessary that I tell you what evil has come upon my house this day—and yet it is hard for me to speak of this matter so soon, and I only do so because of the danger which threatens us. For it came to my ears in a manner which I cannot reveal that the Sons of Uisne had persuaded some of the knights of Ulster to rebel against me, and to make a secret attack in order to wrest the kingdom from me. And it is known to you all how I invited them to return to Ulster, and promised that no harm should befall them in spite of the injury done against me; and how I made my own son Cormac one of the sureties for their safety—" And here Conchobor paused, as if his heart was too heavy for further speech. Loud cries of anger arose among the knights—but Conchobor put up his hand and said, "Nor is that all—for when I called Cormac before me, and asked him if he had knowledge of the truth of this tale, he turned upon me, and said that, being his father he would not lie to me, but that he had given his promise to the Sons of

Uisne to support them in their undertaking, and so he would do whatsoever might come of it—and he rushed forth to join them, taking his vassals with him."

Then the knights of the Red Branch rose to their feet, and cried on Conchobor to give them leave to summon their men, and go out and destroy the Sons of Uisne and all those who had lent themselves to such treachery. And finally Conchobor consented to their demands, but with an appearance of reluctance, as if he could not bring himself to take vengeance on his son—and so the matter was arranged.

Now two days went by with no sign of any attack, and on the third Naoise said to his brothers, "I feel in my heart that our enemies will not wait much longer. Let us sharpen our weapons afresh, and arm ourselves, and go out to meet our foes, not stay lurking here like foxes in a hole."

And so they did. And about noon they all heard the tramp of feet, and soon a great company of knights accompanied by their warriors was seen advancing towards them, and when they saw Naoise and his friends awaiting them a shout went up, "Slay the Sons of Uisne and all with them, and rid Ulster of their treachery." Five hundred or more there must have been come out against a hundred and fifty, and great were the odds against the heroes.

But Naoise and his brothers were in no way disheartened by the sight, and Naoise called out to them, "Let you come on then, and see what death awaits you at our hands! Glad are we to strike blow for blow, and never shall we surrender while life remains to us." Then without further words the two parties fell upon each other, and the din and harsh sounds of battle echoed round the woods and hills—and birds rose up in flocks from the trees and flew screaming away.

All day long the battle raged with unstinted fury—and great deeds were done, and much glory was won by the heroes, for on this little plot of

earth the flower of Ulster's knighthood fought and perished, and an evil day indeed was this for Erin.

For Naoise and his brothers, with their three sureties and their vassals, stood in a circle, and presented a flashing ring of steel to their enemies, and the pile of dead bodies before them grew higher and higher and blood flowed freely as the mountain streams, and neither side would yield.

At last evening came, and Conchobor's men began to draw back a little, and presently their leader called to Naoise for a truce, that they might rest and bind their wounds—but let them resume the fight the next morning—and so it was agreed.

Then the heroes and their small band drew back to the house, and taking it in turns lest further treachery befall, they laved their weary bodies and bound up their wounds, and satisfied their thirst and hunger.

And without taking off their garments they prepared to pass the night in watchfulness, for it was the dark of the moon, and they were determined not to be taken unawares.

And while the heroes rested by their fireside, Deirdre came to Naoise, and sitting by him she said, softly, "O Naoise, my heart's treasure, it was an evil hour when you first saw me, for I have brought you nothing but sorrow, and now I know we shall not see Alba and our dear home again, for it seems to me that you are near your deaths."

And Naoise answered her and said, "My life and my soul, great joy have I had with you in

these past years. And now if I must die, yet I would not have had it otherwise. For rarely can man and woman have known such happiness as we two have known." And he kissed her on the mouth, and bade her take courage for his sake, and valiantly she obeyed him.

Now as the night wore on, steps were heard outside, and presently there was a low knocking on the door, and the voice of Cormac calling on them to open. And when they had done so, they saw Cormac standing there, and by his side a woman's figure hidden in a long black cloak. And Cormac spoke and said, "Here is one who comes to see Deirdre, and will not be turned away." And with that he gave the woman a little push, and she stumbled forward into the light, and the door was shut behind her.

And when she had lifted the covering from her face, whom should they see but Deirdre's old foster-mother and nurse, and the tears running down her face like rains—and she held out her arms timidly as if she expected a rebuff.

Then with a choked cry Deirdre fled to her, and stooped her graceful height, and was gathered into a loving embrace. And in a shaken voice the old woman spoke, and said, "My little babe, my heart's darling—my old eyes have longed to see you once more before I die, but the King forbade me to come to you. But when I heard of the battle, and the dangers and terrors around you, death himself could not have kept me from your side.

And so I came by a secret path I know through the woods, and none hindered me. And now I will stay with you whatever befalls."

Then Naoise came to them, and gave the old woman the kiss of greeting on her withered cheeks, and he said, "Welcome, and more than welcome are you, old mother—for now I can be at ease to know that Deirdre has a woman to comfort her, and a faithful friend. And I trust you not to forsake her should things go ill with me and my brothers on the morrow."

Then Naoise and his brothers threw themselves down to sleep, but sleep had fled from Deirdre, and she and the old nurse sat by the hearth together, and they talked in low whispers of the days that were gone.

And the old woman told Deirdre how she had known in her heart that Conchobor had not forgiven the Sons of Uisne for their deed, and when she had heard of their return, she had thought to find some way of sending them a warning. But Conchobor had sent Laborcham to her dwelling, and the woman had said that the King forbade her to visit Deirdre, and if she disobeyed him it would be the worse for her and her kinsfolk—and so she had waited to see what might befall.

Then Deirdre in her turn told her foster-mother of the happy years in Alba, and of the little house, and the garden, and her four apple trees. And she described the mountains, and the loch, and spoke of the fishing in the boats and of the great eagle she had seen. And she said that the Sons of Uisne were determined to return to that peaceful place if they escaped with their lives from this battle; and the nurse said that old as she was, she would come with them, for never would she be parted from Deirdre again. And so they comforted each other, and sat waiting for the dawn.

And outside the owls cried a warning, and a fox barked in the woods, and a heavy dread filled the heart of Deirdre, and the day seemed long in coming and weighted with terror.

O

11. The Death of the Sons of Uisne

AT LAST the weary night drew back into the west, and a faint, sad light crept slowly and reluctantly across the eastern horizon. But as the light increased, so a thin veil of cloud covered the heavens, dimming the sun's rays, and a soft rain began to fall.

Outside the hut, a small whispering wind murmured for a while among the branches, and then was still. A deep moaning drifted into the silence, as the voice of the ever restless sea took up the song of the wind, and sang a dirge for the sorrows to come.

And within, Naoise and his brothers stood up in their places and put on their war clothing, and took up their weapons. Hardly had they eaten a few oaten cakes, and drunk their fill of mead, than they heard the shouts of their enemies, and the sounds of renewed combat.

Then Naoise came to Deirdre, and kissed her tenderly, and looked into her eyes, and without words turned to the door and went out, holding his long green-blue spear in his right hand, and his shield held aloft in his left hand. And Allain

218

and Ardan in their turn embraced Deirdre, and followed after Naoise.

Once again the harsh noise of combat rose into the still air—the clash of weapons, the cries of the wounded, the fierce shouts of the fighters, the moans of the dying.

But Naoise and his brothers fought in grim silence, their strong arms ceaselessly smiting down their foes, their endurance seemingly tireless. So the morning wore on, and Fiacra met his death with a laugh, and fell surrounded by the swords of his foes; and Cormac too went down into the shades of night defending himself to the last.

Then suddenly, as the fight swayed now this way, now that, and it seemed that Naoise's party gained a small advantage, a strange, evil grey mist began to waver through the trees. At first it came low down, wreathing itself about the legs of the combatants—then it rose to their waists, and Dubthach, who fought near to Allain, called to him, "This is no ordinary thing, but a magic cloud raised by the Druid at Conchobor's behest. What may we do against magic?" And Allain shouted, "Fight, and fight harder—magic cannot hurt us who have right on our side." And so, hearing these words, all the heroes put forth their greatest efforts, and splendid deeds of valour were done in that hour.

But presently the mist thickened, and it rose higher and higher, so that first it reached their shoulders, and then their faces—and then on a sudden all was blotted out, and no man could rightly see another, only dim figures emerging from the gloom, or disappearing into it.

Still the cries of battle arose, but muffled now, and hollow and unreal seemed all the world, as if ghosts stumbled to and fro striking uselessly at each other, nor could men tell their friends from their foes.

Then a great cry rose from where the Sons of Uisne stood, and at that moment the mist began to lift. Quickly it melted, and disappeared into the wood, and the sun shone down, and it showed the bodies of Allain and Ardan locked together in a death-like hold, lying at the feet of Naoise. For it had come about that in the confusion of the mist and the heat of battle, they had slain each other.

Then when Naoise looked down, and saw the bodies of his beloved brothers lying there dead in each other's arms, his heart was hot with fury and anguish. Seeing that his enemies had drawn back a little to give him some respite in his distress, he shouted fierce taunts at them, and leaping into their midst hacked and stabbed with such venom that men fell by the score before him.

But, as hounds worry a noble stag, eager to pull him down, so Naoise's foes harried and pressed about him, until at last, bleeding from a hundred wounds, his eyes dimmed with exhaustion, and his breath whistling in his throat, he fell before them, and lay there in his glorious youthful pride, with the life gone from his strong body, and his sightless eyes staring up at the cool blue of the rain-washed sky.

So died the Sons of Uisne, surrounded by enemies, and vilely slain by treachery in their native land.

Now a melancholy silence fell on wood and field; only the sound of running water, and the mournful cadences of the wind in the pines disturbed the stillness.

Those who were still living moved like wraiths among the dead, and now that the fell deed was accomplished none felt exultant, but a grievous shame seized on the hearts of men as they beheld the fruits of their hatred lying on the ground before them.

Horrible was the sight and smell of blood in that lovely, peaceful place, and confusion took hold of Conchobor's men, so that they forgot that Deirdre, the source of all this bitterness, still lived and without her protectors was at their mercy. So they slunk away from the scene, and at their going a solemn grandeur seemed to fill the valley—and a flock of white birds appeared out of the distance, and hovered over the bodies of Naoise and his brothers, giving vent to piercing, sorrowful cries which echoed to the feet of the hills. And three hinds and a stag came out of the woods, and stood near the fallen heroes, and their heads were bowed as if in mourning.

Then at last, the door of the hut was opened,

and moving slowly, Deirdre and the old nurse came out, and looked at the desolation before them.

So, with drooping head and tearless eyes, Deirdre of the Sorrows sought among the heaps of slain until she came to the place where Naoise and his brothers lay in the long sleep that knows no waking.

Then slowly she fell to her knees, and with her slender white hands she smoothed back the dark, dishevelled hair from Naoise's face, and stooping low, kissed his cold mouth.

Quietly she rose, and said to her foster-mother, "Let us fetch water in a bowl, and linen cloths, and prepare their bodies for the burial."

And with effort and care these two dragged the bodies apart, and laid them on a clean patch of earth near the stream, and there they cleansed away the woeful traces of battle—and Deirdre gazed long on the faces she had loved so well. Then going into the hut, she returned, carrying the little spray of herbs and heather which she had brought from Alba, and this she laid between Naoise's hands, and folded them together on his breast.

And when this was done, and there was no further service she could render to her dear ones, she withdrew into the hut, and closed the door, and remained alone with her grief.

And the old nurse sat before the house so that

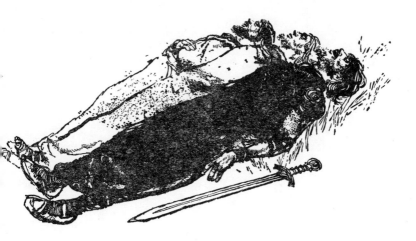

none might disturb Deirdre until her first mourning was ended.

So the evening light filled the valley, and then slowly faded into the west, and the darkening shadows of night began to cover the woods, and blot out the hills, and enshroud the fields.

Thus ended that direful day.

12. The Death of Deirdre

THE NEXT morning soon after daybreak, a trampling of feet was heard in the clearing, and Connor of the Iron Fist, followed by a group of vassals, knocked on the hut door.

The old nurse opened to him, and he wished her a fair day, and asked to speak with the maiden Deirdre.

On hearing his words, Deirdre stood up, and called to the nurse to let him enter, and when he was before her, he said, "I am the bearer of greetings from Conchobor the King. He wishes me to say to you that now the Sons of Uisne are dead, the cause of his anger against you is removed. It is his desire to show you all honour, and he has a dwelling prepared for you near his own halls. And when the time of mourning is past, he will take you to wife. What message shall I take to the King, O Deirdre?"

Then Deirdre smiled—a strange and dreadful smile on such a lovely face—and she replied, "You may take this message to King Conchobor. I thank him for his courteous greetings, but until the burials are over it is no time to speak of marriage. Nor will I leave this place unless I am taken by force, until the Sons of Uisne are laid in an honourable grave."

Then Connor bowed low, and departed, and so that day went by with none to disturb them.

The next morning the sun rose bright and undimmed by cloud in the radiant east, and cast his glorious light over the jewel-like brilliance of Erin's mountains and valleys—never had there been such a depth of purple in the shadows on the hills, or such rich blue where the sun's rays touched them; nor such flaming crimsons, oranges and gold on the trees. And the only sounds of mourning to be heard were the sad, wild and beautiful cries of the gulls circling between sea and land.

Now on this day, very early, there was a knocking on the hut door, and a man stood there who said that he had been sent by Conchobor. "The King," said he, "has bidden me to tell you that the burial of all those slain in the battle will be at the noon hour, when the sun is high in the heavens, and he will send a bodyguard to accompany you to the burying-place."

Then Deirdre bowed her head, and bade the man give her greetings to Conchobor, and answer that she would gladly go with the escort when the hour came.

When the man had gone, Deirdre went out to the stream, and bathed herself from head to foot, and when that was done, she entered the hut, and helped by the old woman she put on clean linen

226

under-garments, and a dress of snowy whiteness, embroidered with tiny butterflies. She put her golden bracelet on her right arm, and on her left hand she wore the ring of gold which Naoise had given her—and over all she wore a cloak of deep, rich blue, leaving her glorious golden hair unbound.

Then she seated herself in the chair where Naoise used to sit, and the nurse sat in Deirdre's seat, and so they waited for the coming of the King's men.

Time that was no time, but an emptiness, passed, and once more they heard feet approaching the house, and Deirdre bade the nurse throw open the door, and she came to the threshold, and stood there.

And in a while a company of vassals appeared, all in white tunics, and they went to where the heroes lay, and lifted them up, and laying each on his shield they carried the bodies solemnly away.

And after them came the knights of the King's bodyguard, clothed in war apparel, and leading a white horse, and the leader bowed to Deirdre, and asked her to mount the horse, and gave her his hand to aid her. And so the procession started, with the old nurse following in the rear.

At last they came into a wide open space, with the mountains looking down from their great height, and in the distance the silver-surfaced loch glinting in the sunlight. And here, in the soft green grass, the graves had been dug for all the

227

heroes slain on that woeful day—but a separate grave had been dug for the Sons of Uisne.

And standing near the burying-place was a mighty company; King Conchobor, in his cloak of royal crimson, and his tunic embroidered with golden threads, and all the knights of the Red Branch in battle array, carrying their shields and spears, and the kinsfolk and friends of those who had perished in the battle. And in this manner they did honour to the dead heroes.

Then when all were assembled, the Druid stood out in his white ceremonial robes, and made a speech in praise of the fallen, and his words were as the rushing of a great wind in the tree-tops; and when he had ended, all the knights lifted their spears, and clashed their shields together, so that the sound rolled round the plain like thunder, and was echoed from the distant hills.

And when the echoes had died away, certain men stepped forward, and lifting the bodies, one by one, placed them in the graves, and so left them.

Then, before any could move to fill in the graves, Deirdre stepped forward, and stood alone by the place where the Sons of Uisne were laid. And in silence she looked down upon them, taking her last farewell of Naoise as he rested there, his eyes closed as in sleep, his shield and green spear by his side, and his hands still holding the spray of blossoms.

Then, lifting her head she began to speak, and these were her words:

"There is no joy without the Children of Uisne,
O grievous not to be in your company,
Three sons of a king who helped the helpless,
Today without speech on the bank of the grave.

The three bears of the Isles of Britain,
The three hawks of the hill of Cuillinn,
The three to whom heroes would yield,
Three to whom hirelings would pay homage.

The three birds of loveliest hues
That came over the ocean of billows,
The three Sons of Uisne of beautiful mien,
Like three swans on the waves floating.

I will go, joyfully, proudly,
To the three nobles most beloved,
My time behind them is not long,
Nor a coward's death is mine.

Ye Children of Uisne over there,
Ye lying together sole to sole,
If dead could lie closer for a living
Ye would lie closer for me.

Move hither, O Naoise of my love!
Let Ardan draw nearer to Allain,
If dead had understanding
Ye would make room for me."

Thus she ended, and so speaking she drooped
and swayed, and before any could put out a hand

she had fallen forward into the grave—and when they lifted her up, behold, she was dead. Thus she escaped for ever from the thraldom of Conchobor's power, and the malice of men—and all the evil that had befallen was brought to nought. For although Conchobor shook with helpless fury when he realised that she was out of his reach, there was nothing more he could do to harm her—so he ordered that she should be laid beside the Sons of Uisne, and it was done, and so perished Deirdre of the Sorrows, in all her beauty and youth.

And no man or woman who stood there on that day ever forgot the face of Deirdre, or the words she spoke.

Thus was the prophecy of the Druid fulfilled, and many proud heroes lost their lives, and Ulster was plunged into lasting grief.

And after a time it is said that two young pine trees sprang up over the burial place of Deirdre and the Sons of Uisne; and as they grew, their branches twined lovingly together, and a pair of hawks had their nest there each year.

And soon people began to say that at certain times, when the wind whispered in the branches, they could hear the voices of Deirdre and Naoise talking together in love and happiness. And when this tale came to Conchobor's ears, his anger knew no bounds, and he ordered the two young trees to be cut down and burnt. And this was done.

But the next spring, two more sprang up in

their place, and as they grew, so their branches twined together—and once again the voices of the lovers were heard on quiet summer evenings. And this time the King dared not destroy the trees, for already folk were murmuring angrily at what they deemed to be his persecution of the innocent dead.

And now, with the long passing of time, the place where the Sons of Uisne and Deirdre lie has been forgotten; but perhaps if you visit Erin, and are on Ulster's shores, you may chance upon two pine trees leaning close together, and hear the voices of Deirdre and Naoise laughing among the branches.

And so the story ends.